THE OAKWOOD PRESS

GW00642999

SIR SYDNEY CAMM

From Biplanes &
'Hurricanes' to 'Harriers'

by
J.E. Chacksfield
FBIS, FRAeS, AFAIAA, C. Eng

'Aircraft design is an art, not a science'
Sir Sydney Camm

THE OAKWOOD PRESS

© Oakwood Press 2010 & the Estate of John Chacksfield

British Library Cataloguing in Publication Data
A Record for this book is available from the British Library
ISBN 978 0 85361 698 6
Typeset by Oakwood Graphics.
Repro by PKmediaworks, Cranborne, Dorset.
Printed by Cambrian Printers, Aberystwyth, Ceredigion.

This picture of a Mk I 'Hunter' gives a good plan view of this classic aircraft.

BAE Systems

Published by The Oakwood Press (Usk), P.O. Box 13, Usk, Mon., NP15 1YS.
E-mail: sales@oakwoodpress.co.uk
Website: www.oakwoodpress.co.uk

Contents

The 'Sea Fury' FB Mk2. WF619. The final Hawker piston-engined fighter.   *BAE Systems*

Foreword

In October 2006 - in my capacity as Librarian of the Royal Aeronautical Society (RAeS) - I was asked by John Chacksfield CEng, FRAeS, 'Has there ever been published a full biography of Sir Sydney Camm?'

In my reply I noted that the closest there was to a biography of Sir Sydney Camm was *Sydney Camm and the Hurricane: Perspectives on the Master Fighter Designer and his Finest Achievement* edited by John W. Fozard (Airlife Publishing Ltd, 1991) which is effectively a collection of essays about Camm's life and work.

That Camm had been 'overlooked' is not unusual for whereas there are literally thousands of books available on individual aircraft types - and a more limited number of general histories on aircraft companies over the years - books on the leading personalities and captains of industry who formed and shaped these companies are few and far between. Camm is atypical of this trend; there are a number of books about the Hawker designs, particularly concerning the 'Hurricane' - the main reference work on the aircraft being Francis K. Mason's *The Hawker Hurricane* (Aston Publications Ltd, 1987) who also compiled the standard work on the company *Hawker Aircraft since 1920* (Putnam Aeronautical Books, 1991 [Third edition]) - but little on the contribution of Camm himself.

The Chief Designer for the Hawker company from 1925, Camm's early designs included his famous series of military biplanes - the 'Hart' and 'Fury' - before in 1933 he proposed designing a low wing monoplane fighter which culminated in the 'Hurricane'. After initial problems his later wartime designs - the 'Typhoon' and 'Tempest' - were adapted into effective ground attack aircraft and fighters. Post-war Camm turned to jet aircraft, first with the 'Sea Hawk' then the swept-wing 'Hunter', his supersonic successor to the 'Hunter' - the 'P.1121' - being partially built when cancelled by the British Government. In the 1960s Camm became interested in the possibilities of vertical take-off, and with Stanley Hooker of Bristol Siddeley conceived the design that led to the 'Harrier', a world leader in vertical and/or short take-off and landing (V/STOL) aircraft design.

Camm's life story is recounted in detail by John Chacksfield in the pages that follow which helps to fill one of the 'gaps' in the historical record of the development of the aircraft industry in Britain.

Brian Riddle
Librarian, Royal Aeronautical Society

'Typhoon' FB Mk Ib.   *BAE Systems*

4

Introduction

For many years I was a Project Office man, first at the de Havilland works, Hatfield, following a five-year apprenticeship at that site, and later at the British Aircraft Corporation (BAC), Warton, plant. The Hatfield position was as one of the six chosen technical staff to form an Advanced Projects Office team to investigate and scheme what future aircraft were to be considered for the company to design, whether civil or military and, hopefully, build. Before the BAC job materialized I spent time as Deputy Chief Aerodynamicist of Short Brothers and Harland's Light Aircraft Division followed by landing the position of running the Production Flight Test and Certification matters at British Executive and General Aviation (BEAGLE) after which I spent five years as Chief Aerodynamicist at Miles Aviation and Transport (R&D) Ltd. So, by the time I got to BAC at Warton I had had a good range of experience behind me, and launched into development work in the Advanced Project Office involving studies of developments of 'Jaguar' and 'Tornado', followed by what eventually became 'Eurofighter' early project work.

This latter task, in my day, was the key to the future prosperity of a company and it is worth noting here that in the 1920s and 1930s such work was part and parcel of the design team's output as a whole. The quality of the resulting aircraft depended largely on the leadership, advice and guidance of the Chief Designer who, in those days, played an important part in deciding the next development. The decisions he had to make were crucial and those beneath him had to be well-chosen to be effective at their job.

Sydney Camm was one such man who, under a sometimes autocratic and out-spoken exterior, was an extremely capable and practical engineer with an eye for good design. Like so many I have worked under he was, despite his blunt approach, a good leader, encouraging those of his team who showed promise. His own rise to the top had been in many respects a speedy one in the days when opportunities to move upwards were sometimes hard to come by. This latter aspect alone indicates a good mind capable of assimilating facts and features for future use where applicable.

As with so many other eminent people, Camm had a patron who realized his potential and used it to full advantage. This was (Sir) T.O.M. Sopwith. Sopwith, of the same generation as Camm, was the complete opposite of him in background. He came from a relatively wealthy family and could indulge in his passion for speed. Motorbikes, cars and racing yachts were his first steeds, followed by ballooning, before turning to aeroplanes. This latter was approached in the unorthodox but quite logical method of buying himself an aeroplane and teaching himself to fly with it at Brooklands in 1910. He proved a natural pilot and proceeded to enter competitions wherever they appeared, winning a considerable amount of prize money in the process. Following a trip to the USA in 1911, where he also won more prize money, he set up a business to repair and modify aeroplanes at Brooklands in 1912. By 1913 he had begun to build his own designs and extended his premises to a disused roller skating rink in Kingston, which he soon added to by acquiring a site along the road, followed by leasing a substantial factory built by the Government, No. 1 Aircraft Factory, at nearby Ham during World War I. These sites resulted in the delivery of some 14,000 aircraft to the services in World War I. One of the acknowledged pioneers in the British aviation sphere, Sopwith recognized the

The Brooklands flight sheds in 1912. The nearest three are those where Tom Sopwith began his aircraft business. *BAE Systems*

genius behind the outspoken comments emanating from Camm and gave him solid encouragement in his efforts. This encouragement was to produce the conditions for the growth of Sopwith's company, by then renamed the H.G. Hawker Engineering Company, in the 1920s and early 1930s, into the Hawker Siddeley conglomerate in the mid-1930s.

Like myself, Camm came into aviation via the hobby of building and flying model aircraft, so in this way, at least, I can identify with him. In fact, one of his quotes from a broadcast made in 1942 starts in that vein: 'I am one of those lucky individuals who've been able to convert a boyhood hobby into a profession, as I commenced making model aeroplanes when a schoolboy'. His greatest achievement was, undoubtedly, the creation of the Hawker 'Hurricane' fighter, although there are those who place this accolade on the 'Hart' biplane of 1929, which spawned a series of designs to fill the needs of the RAF in the 1930s and financed the expansion of Sopwith's empire. However, the 'Hurricane', which during the Battle of Britain shot down more enemy planes than the combined scores of all other means, whether air-, sea- or land-based, is the recognized aircraft generally associated with Camm. It, together with the 'Spitfires', turned the tide in that crucial conflict of 1940 and enabled us to continue on the path to victory in 1945. This country has much to thank Camm for.

He then went on from his wartime success to enter the jet age with the 'Sea Hawk', followed by the classic 'Hunter' and was preparing to see the 'Harrier' into its production phase when he died, still in harness, in 1966.

Camm was by all accounts sometimes a rather difficult person to work with. His sudden outspoken outbursts were quite something to weather, in fact Sir Thomas Sopwith is recorded as saying: 'I can't imagine why his men put up with him. He was a genius - but quite impossible'. However, under this bluff exterior, he could be a most kindly and considerate person should a member of his staff take him into their confidence on a personal matter. A perfectionist where detail design was concerned Camm, in his early career as Chief Designer, personally checked every drawing before it was issued to the shop floor. Yet where would this country have been without his 'Hurricane' fighter in those

The Sopwith 'Camel', the top scoring British fighter of World War I.   *BAE Systems*

crucial days of the Battle of Britain? Matters could have turned out to our disadvantage had he not had complete control of the design matters from inception in 1933, which ensured that adequate numbers of aircraft were available to stem the Luftwaffe onslaught in 1940.

Chief Designers came in all shades of personality. Their main driving ambition was to further the provision of aircraft for a wide range of tasks in times of war and peace. R.E. Bishop of de Havilland and 'Comet' fame was a quiet unassuming man with a determination of purpose and clear mind who knew what he wanted, but was only accessible via a chain of assistants. George Miles, of Miles Aviation & Transport, always very approachable, continuously looked forward to new pastures but was held back by financial constraints. He did, however, give his key men a very free hand in their tasks and would back their schemes if he saw merit in them. Apart from the difference in approachability, combining the rest of the attributes of the above two Designers, and adding explosive outbursts, one has (Sir) Sydney Camm at his work.

Camm, like other Chief Designers, recruited some graduates with good engineering degrees, despite a cautious approach to people with lots of qualifications. Whether or not this latter was a deliberate matter, placing such persons in his design team certainly gave him people capable of dealing with complex structural analysis as new or innovative schemes appeared in his drive for light weight and ease of production. It certainly was most useful when analysis of stressed skin and monocoque structures entered the design sphere from the mid-thirties onward. It was as though, recognizing his own lack of academic qualifications, if he had such people under him following his orders, the job would still be under his own control. His delegation in this respect was exemplary and the caution understandable.

Whilst the internet has provided much information, this narrative could not have been written without help from many quarters, in particular from various members of the Hawker Association who had worked under Camm, notably, Ralph Hooper who laid the foundation of the unique 'Harrier'. Barry Pegram and Gordon Jefferson also provided little snippets of information and contacts which enabled the story to be told in greater detail. And I must not forget Ambrose Barber and Chris Farara for their comments on the draft text, many of which were noted and worked in. The vast majority of the illustrations were provided by BAe Systems Heritage Centre, who gave me free access to their copious archives which I found residing in the old 'Black Sheds' at the historic site of Farnborough.

I make no apology for the fact that part of the text of this biography reads like a company history. This is because Camm's professional life was inextricably bound up in the growth of Hawker Engineering into the Hawker Siddeley Group, which may well not have happened without his designs selling so well to provide some of the impetus for that growth.

This, then, is a biography of Sir Sydney Camm from the viewpoint of an aeronautical engineer who finished his career at British Aerospace, Kingston and later Farnborough, between 1983 and 1995, as a member of the design team of whom several had been under Camm in his later years before his sudden death. Regrettably, I never had the chance to meet the man. However, those who are still around to remember his presence do so with a mixture of pride and awe when talking about their experiences under Sir Sydney.

Chapter One

The Early Days

There is a row of terraced houses in Alma Road, Windsor, once named Bounty Terrace. Number 2 of this row, long since renumbered to 10 Alma Road, had a blue plaque installed in 1986. This blue plaque was to commemorate the fact that Sir Sydney Camm was born and lived there as a boy. Sadly, thieves have seen fit to remove the plaque on two occasions, it being eventually recovered the first time but not the second. It has since been replaced by a new one.

A great deal of controversy on the future of this block of houses has raged for some years in Windsor, with the local council putting forward plans to demolish them to make way for a car park. They lay empty for several years before the council's ambitions collapsed and the properties were renovated and, thankfully, are occupied again.

It was in number 2 Bounty Terrace that Frederick Camm, a carpenter and joiner by trade, lived with his wife Maria from 1890. Legend has it that his grandfather had been named Cam until a spelling error on prize certificates awarded by a Royal Association had listed the surname as Camm. This resulted in the comment by the old man that: 'What is good enough for the Queen is good enough for me' and the surname remained thus, for that arm of the family, to this day. How true this fact may be is open to speculation.

Frederick Camm was, apart from being a highly-skilled carpenter and joiner, a clever person. He hailed from nearby Egham, as did his wife, and had obtained his education at the Great Park school where the headmaster wanted him to become a school teacher. However, the Camm family were not sufficiently well off to finance that and he was apprenticed to Brown Brothers, the well-known carriage builders of the day in Windsor. His skills obtained from this apprenticeship were such that he could support his family, and between 1893 and 1912, twelve children were to be born, one of whom died in infancy.

Four doors along Bounty Terrace, at number 6, lived Frederick's elder brother Arthur, also a carpenter and joiner, with his wife Florence and son Arthur.

On 5th August, 1893, Frederick and Maria produced their first child, a son Sydney, and by the turn of the century had added Frederick (1895), Edith (1897) and Charles (1900) to the brood. Young Frederick (F.J. Camm) was to become well-known as the editor of the famous 'Practical' series of magazines, but it is Sydney we need to turn our attention to.

His childhood was a conventional one, with his father's skills as a carpenter ensuring that the family was adequately provided for. As the family grew in number, the small house was becoming crowded but it was by all accounts a happy home. Sydney started his education at the local primary school, where his above average abilities were soon noted. This won him a place at the Royal Free School for the last years of his education. This school had been founded in 1705 and, whilst covering all abilities, drew its pupils mainly from working

The Royal Free School, Windsor, in 1902. Sydney Camm is second from the right in the
second row.   *By permission of the current Headmaster*

class homes. In 1906 his results in the classroom were such that he was made a
Foundation Scholar, which meant that his fees were paid and a free uniform
provided at this establishment. The signs were that he could go places in the
future.

His education stopped at the age of 15, when he left school to enter into an
apprenticeship as a carpenter, intending to get a skill under his belt for the future
and hopefully follow in the footsteps of his father. The apprenticeship was with a
firm of local builders, Butcher & Hendry of Grove Road, Windsor, and the
apprentices pay in those days began at one shilling per week, rising by a further
shilling per week as each year was completed. However, some reporting of the
development of a successful powered man-carrying aeroplane had been filtering
through from the United States since 1904. The Wright Brothers, Orville and
Wilbur, achieved their goal of controlled, manned, powered flight in December
1903 and went on developing their revolutionary machine.

On 15th December, 1905 Patrick Y. Alexander, a keen balloonist and amateur
aviation enthusiast, read a letter from the Wright brothers, whom he had first
met in 1902, to the Aeronautical Society in London, describing their recent
flights. One of these flights, on 20th September, 1904, took place at Huffman
Prairie, Dayton, Ohio and was the first powered and controlled flight over a
circular path, with the aeroplane arriving back at its starting point. Considering
it was only a little over nine months since their first successful series of powered
controlled flights at Kitty Hawk, this was a magnificent achievement. Three
people witnessed this unique event, Orville Wright (Wilbur was flying the

machine), a Mr Taylor, a neighbour of the Wrights', and a local apiarist, Amos Ives Root. The press had been invited to attend but had left a few days earlier after some problems with the 'Flyer' prevented any take-off. (An edited extract from Root's writing on the event is to be found in the Appendix.)

Shortly after his reading of the letter, P.Y. Alexander carried out some aviation science teaching, at the invitation of the headmaster, at the Imperial Science College in Windsor. It seems probable that he could have used selected quotations from the letters in his talks, or even some of Root's observations. Although Sydney Camm was not able to attend this college, he was still at this time at the Royal Free School, quite possibly the news of Alexander's revelations filtered out to some in Windsor, himself included.

Another fact which may well have added to Sydney's interest in matters aeronautical was that behind the row of houses in Alma Road lay the Royal Windsor Gaslight Works which were often used when balloonists required a fill of gas for their aerial mounts. So he, as a small child, would have seen the occasional balloon setting off on its aerial journey.

By 1907 the Wright brothers were to be found in Paris with the latest version of their 'Flyer', preparing to arrange some demonstration flights which were to astonish the aviation pioneers of Europe. This eventually found its way into the newspapers and the limited aeronautical press of the day.

The British authorities at that time were quite reticent to encourage aviation too strongly at that time. Some members of the Government realized that a viable aeroplane would destroy the immunity of the British Isles to interference or, even attack, from abroad. At that time this immunity was assured by a large and powerful Navy. On the Continent, however, matters were much more open. Several European countries were vying for the Wrights 'secrets' and created a log-jam of conflicting requests for demonstrations in 1907. The 'Flyer' remained crated-up in store in France and the Wrights departed for the USA in December, and were to return the next year for their demonstration programme. However, a seed was sown and the promise of successful aviation aroused latent desires in several British entrepreneurs, drawn largely from the membership of the Aero Club, up to then primarily involved with ballooning.

When eventually demonstrated in 1908-1909 the 'Flyer' showed that the Wrights' ideas were clearly way ahead of their counterparts on the European side of the Atlantic. Those aviation enthusiasts who were keen to emulate them now had a definite target to aim for in their pioneering efforts.

Sydney's interest in aviation began after seeing, in a local model shop, some drawings of a model of the Wright biplane published by the model engineering firm of Bassett Lowke. He bought a set of the drawings and, from them, made a model. It did not fly very successfully, which only increased his determination to succeed. In 1909 the *Daily Mail* published some drawings of the Bleriot machine which successfully crossed the English Channel in that year. Camm also made a model from these but one gathers that this was also a poor flyer. A spin-off from this led to him becoming increasingly involved in the hobby of building and flying model aeroplanes which had, by now, been around for some years. Ever since Sir George Cayley had used models in the early 19th century to try out his own designs, in fact.

Sydney had entered into the building and flying of model aeroplanes eagerly as he left school and started his apprenticeship in 1908. The wood-working skill he was learning fitted nicely with his model making. So, following the accepted lines of other's models he built a series of models which, after some development, flew satisfactorily. He learnt the importance of lightweight construction and the basics of the stability engendered by tail or foreplane surface placement and acceptable size. They were all powered by elastic driving a carved wooden propeller and at weekends were often seen in the fields around Windsor and Eton and also Windsor Great Park. As Sir Frederick Handley Page was to write in connection with the design of aircraft: 'No more certain way of acquainting oneself with the alpha and omega exists than the making of model aeroplanes'. Sydney's brother Frederick joined him in this hobby and the two boys set about supplying a local shop, Herberts, in Eton High Street, with finished examples for sale, which were advertised as 'will really fly'. Shortly after this they found that they could get a better profit by cutting out the middle man and got direct sales to the Eton College boys. Delivery had to be made at night via a string lowered from the dormitories. Herberts were not amused! The news that Sydney would make model aircraft to order soon spread to the Eton boys' parents and often their elegant mothers would call at the Alma Road house to order a model for their son's birthday.

In 1911 one particular event spurred him on in his interests; this was T.O.M. Sopwith's flight over Windsor Castle, circling the Round Tower and the subsequent landing on the East Terrace. Little did he realise then that Sopwith was to become a key person in his future career.

Tom Sopwith in his Howard Wright aircraft, 1912.   *BAE Systems*

As he progressed through his apprenticeship days, the interest aroused locally by Camm's success with model aeroplanes led to the Windsor Model Aeroplane Club (WMAC) being formed by himself, his brother Frederick and a group of local enthusiasts. Sydney was, by 1912, elected Secretary of the WMAC. The club's activities were reported in the aviation magazine *Flight* by Frederick in its early days, particularly when a project for a man-carrying glider was proposed. Much of the WMAC work was reported as a regular series of notes to the magazine, which were then edited and published. Frederick was led into journalism by these reports and he was to become a well-known journalist involved in technical magazines, starting as model editor of *Flight*. After some basic drawings of the glider had been produced, the membership set to with gusto and by December 1912 had completed building their first design. Just how much input Camm had in this exercise is not absolutely clear, but his woodworking skills would have been used well and, one suspects, his forceful personality would have   come to the fore. Also he had, during his apprenticeship, been enrolled in evening classes of working drawings at the Prince Albert Consort Mechanics Institute in Windsor, so quite probably he had a large part in preparing the drawings. The glider was a biplane of 32 ft span and weighed just 66 lb. Sydney clearly recognized the importance of keeping the weight to a minimum, a feature which was to be found throughout his aviation career that was to come. They attempted to fly it but it was not successful. However, much had been learnt in the process and a second, much improved glider was built, this time having a better control system. From this last bit of information one is led to think that the first glider was designed for control primarily by weight-shift only, always a difficult task. The second example was again a biplane, of 25 ft span and wing area 225 sq. ft, and weighed just 75 lb. This version had a rudimentary control system. They flew this successfully in May 1913, the 'pilot' being young Charles Camm who was instructed not to touch the controls. According to contemporary accounts it was reasonably successful - at least Charles returned to terra firma intact!

The WMAC became a well-known club in aviation circles and exhibited some of the models constructed by members at the Aero Show at Olympia in February 1913. Such was the interest in them that even the King inspected them and indicated his interest in seeing them fly. Also in the summer of that year Sydney competed at a model aircraft meeting at Hendon, coming in third place with his entry.

The interest aroused by the above excursions into aircraft design by Sydney and his colleagues of the WMAC led him, at weekends, to cycle over to Brooklands to watch the developments at this cradle of British Aviation. Quite often his brother Frederick would accompany him on these jaunts, as he would on the longer haul to Hendon aerodrome where other early flying took place. In September 1913 they were lucky enough to witness the Frenchman M. Pegoud demonstrate looping the loop in his Bleriot monoplane at Brooklands. Pegoud, having demonstrated this, then proceeded to climb to a moderate height before entering an outside loop, or 'bunt', into inverted flight. This latter caused some of the men present to gasp in horror and several ladies fainted, anticipating a disastrous crash during this unorthodox manoeuvre. Sydney clearly got close to the aircraft there for he could be found back at Windsor giving critical accounts of those inspected and their

Sydney Camm and one of his many model aircraft at Byfleet in 1912.   *BAE Systems*

respective capabilities to the WMAC members. These, of course, were powered examples and this naturally led to the WMAC starting to develop a powered aircraft using a 20 hp Cowley two-stroke engine. They located the engine in Belfast in the ownership of a Miss Bland who was prepared to sell it for £25. It had previously belonged to A.V. Roe who found it of too low a power for his use.

There is an amusing account of an unanticipated test run of this engine made by some members of the WMAC after it had been rebuilt to replace some missing parts. One Sunday it was taken into the garden shed of No. 10, Alma Road and firmly bolted to the workbench, the propeller attached, a little fuel introduced to lubricate it; being a two-stroke the lubricating oil was mixed in with the petrol for distribution in the workings, whereupon the members present took turns to swing the propeller. To their surprise, the engine eventually fired and shattered the peace of the Sunday afternoon. Its vibration started the bench moving around the shed as the frantic members tried to stop it, all the time dodging the flailing propeller. They eventually succeeded, by which time the local police had arrived to administer a severe warning.

But before this power-plant could be used for its intended purpose the onset of World War I brought this exercise to a halt and the aircraft was never finished.

Camm had also taken advantage of being close to London to visit the aeronautical exhibitions held there, which added to his growing interest in such matters. At these events he was able to view close at hand the very latest in aeroplane developments and took particular note of the varying types of constructional methods in use by the leading designers. He made copious notes and sketches for his own reference. These notes were later to be put into print in a book, *Aeroplane Construction*, which, but for World War I could have been published, but this was delayed until 1919. The book shows a considerable knowledge of the intricacies of aeroplane construction, comparing the various methods employed by the early designers. As an example of the construction of such machines it is excellent and its many chapters cover each component and system of early aircraft in considerable detail. His knowledge gained from the study of aeroplanes on display at exhibitions and in and around the flight sheds at Brooklands shows a good retentive memory, an analytical mind and an instinctive appreciation of good design methods. One begins to understand his abilities which resulted in his eventually gaining the Chief Designer. Also, during World War I, he was allowed time off for access to the captured German aircraft on display at the Agricultural Hall, Islington where he gathered much extra information, a lot of which is to be found in *Aeroplane Construction*.

The bicycle was Camm's main means of transport in these early days. A new one could cost seven pounds, this being a considerable sum to accumulate in those days, particularly on an apprentice's wages. However, Sydney managed to gather the required amount together in a relatively short time and once the bicycle was purchased he immediately began to use it for his trips to Brooklands and elsewhere, to feed his insatiable desire to view matters aeronautical. The determination to achieve his aim of gathering as much information as possible showed through in all this.

The war having begun shortly after Camm's completion of his apprenticeship, he began to cast around for employment, finding it with the firm of aircraft producers

Martinsydes. They had a factory in nearby Woking and flying sheds at Brooklands and were looking for woodworkers to bolster their production staff. This company, created by H.P. Martin and George Handasyde, had been formed in 1908 to build aeroplanes and struggled along on small contracts until the war appeared when matters took off. Camm applied his carpentry skills to the construction of several Martinsyde designs which were on the drawing boards as war broke out. Very soon George Handasyde noted that this carpenter was not only a good craftsman but that he had a good grasp of engineering drawing and matters relevant to the design of aircraft. Now, Handasyde was reckoned to be one of the leading aircraft designers of the days and, coupled to this, was one of those people who took note of the abilities of those under him. Looking ahead he realized that some senior people in the company, including himself, would eventually need to be replaced, and made sure that up-and-coming young men with good abilities were encouraged to widen their knowledge. In other words potential successors for a wide range of tasks would be nurtured and prepared for a move up in status as opportunities occurred. Such occasions were rare, but Sydney grasped the opportunity eagerly.

Martinsydes was increasingly busy as a company, for in addition to designing its own aircraft, large sub-contracts were obtained from the War Office for the construction of both 'BE.2c' and 'SE.5A' aircraft. Just prior to the war they had been designing and building, under strict secrecy, a monoplane for Gustav Hamel to use in an attempt to fly across the Atlantic Ocean. The first person to achieve this would be eligible for the £10,000 prize offered by Lord Northcliffe, the owner of the *Daily Mail*. This was a large machine by the standards of the day, the span being almost 70 ft, with the wings being braced by a system of king-posts and wires to stiffen the monoplane layout. Hamel was, despite his surname, British, and an early pioneer aviator holding the Royal Aero Club aviator's certificate No. 64, gained on 14th February, 1911 on a Bleriot monoplane. In 1912 he came second in the Aerial Derby and first in 1913. He had also flown from Dover to Cologne non-stop in April 1913, and had given two Royal Command flying exhibitions at Windsor. On 23rd May, 1913 he took off from Calais intending to return to England but never arrived. An air and sea search found no trace of him or his machine. To this day his disappearance remains a mystery, more particularly with the Channel being such a busy part of the seaways.

One of the first Martinsyde aircraft in which Camm had a small part to play was the 'G100', or 'Elephant', as it was dubbed because of its size. The 'G100' was powered by a 120 hp Beardmore engine and proved under-powered, slow and had poor maneuverability, but found use as a bomber to a limited extent. A further variant, the 'G102' was also produced, this time with a 160 hp Beardmore engine, but with a top speed of 103 mph and its sole defensive armament just a single Lewis gun mounted in a awkward place for the pilot, on top of the centre-section, it gained a reputation as 'Albatross fodder'. It served in France and the Middle East with a total of 270 being manufactured.

After this initial disappointment the sub-contract work took precedence, but the little design group concentrated on developing a range of fighter aircraft, the 'F1', 'F2', and 'F3', leading to the 'F4' 'Buzzard'. With so much design work to be done, Handasyde took Camm from the stores, to where he had been promoted from the shop floor, into the drawing office as a draughtsman. The shop floor became a thing of the past, it was to be design from now on.

It was shortly before this promotion that Sydney married. His bride was Hilda Rose Starnes, the sister of an old colleague of his WMAC days. They had known each other for three years after having first met when Hilda had accompanied her brother, J.G. Starnes, who had been one of the early members of the WMAC, to some of the flying meetings. She was just one year his senior and Sydney found her good company and they increasingly could be found together in spare moments. He finally popped the question, to which the answer was a clear yes, and they married at Christmas 1915 in the parish church of Wooburn, Buckinghamshire, and set up home at Byfleet, conveniently between the Woking works and Brooklands.

With all the sub-contract diversions, the 'F1', 'F2', and 'F3' prototypes were designed and built but, at first, no production orders materialized. However, the exercise was a useful one in that the 'F3', in 1917, was considered to be one of the best single-seat fighters to emerge during the war. The 'F3' 'Buzzard' was powered by a Rolls-Royce 'Falcon' engine of 275 hp and, after trials at Martlesham Heath which proved its superiority over all current types pitted against it, was ordered into quantity production at the end of 1917 to the tune of 1,300 aircraft. Then supplies of the 'Falcon' were diverted to the Bristol 'Fighter' and the 'Buzzard' had to be re-designed to take the Hispano-Suiza '8fb' of 300 hp, becoming the 'F4' in the process. This delayed production somewhat and only 370 were built, most of them after the war's end. So it never got into active service. Many were sold overseas, with the Russians buying 100, and the company slimmed down at the war's end and turned to building motorcycles to try to stay afloat.

Through all this fighter development work Camm gained much invaluable knowledge into the art of aircraft design and Handasyde could see a clear sign of a thorough understanding of design features, both aerodynamic and structural. As the company shrank he ensured that Camm was kept on the small design staff.

Camm's younger brother Charles, who had been called up for military service and had taken part in the battle of the Somme, in which he had been wounded, returned safely at the end of the war much to the family's delight. So all was not doom and gloom. Sydney Camm escaped the call-up because he was engaged on work of importance to the war effort.

In 1918, with some experience on the design side, Camm had been elected as an Associate Member of the Royal Aeronautical Society. This was indicative of his competence on design matters achieved in a relatively short time. Both Handasyde and Martin had a hand in this election.

With work at a low level, some of Camm's spare time in 1919 was spent going through the draft text produced from his old exhibition notes gathered before the war to see how aircraft constructional methods had changed in the interim. The net result was that he started collating his information and bringing in some newer data gathered during his time in the Design Office and culminated in a reference book, the only one to his name, *Aeroplane Construction*, which, as mentioned earlier, was published in 1919.

The end of the war placed many aircraft companies into a quandary. No longer were there lucrative military contracts and the Government of the day was intent on reducing the Air Force to a fraction of its wartime size. To keep the company viable Martinsydes turned to motorcycle production, as did the Sopwith Aviation Company in nearby Kingston. Aircraft development now centred round a limited civil market and specialized racing machines. Whilst Martinsydes continued limited aircraft work in peacetime, Camm, in 1920, had been asked to develop the Buzzard fighter into a racing machine to be entered into the Gordon Bennett Trophy race for that year. He cut the span down to 20 feet and it won the Aerial Derby at Hendon at the high average speed of 153 mph, which was considerably faster than any current fighter. Despite the short span, the aircraft handled well, but was not successful in the next entry, the Gordon Bennett Trophy race, for which it had been designed. However, it gave Camm some considerable insight in getting a high performance machine produced and flown, and also gave him valuable experience in the quest for speed.

The following chapters are not a comprehensive account of Camm's individual designs during his career, but more an account of how he developed his own particular style of fighter aircraft designs. Therefore many of the aircraft mentioned in the following text will be those involving key features of his design methodology which continuously improved the range of types through the years, from biplane to monoplane and from piston engines to jet power-plants.

Camm was ultimately responsible for over 50 aircraft designs which, in terms of production quantity, in peace and war, totalled some 27,000 aircraft over the 41 years of his design leadership at Kingston.

Sydney Camm and Hilda. They are on a Martinsyde motorcycle combination. This particular model appeared in 1922.   *BAE Systems*

Chapter Two

The Continued Climb

As the 1920s began, Camm realized that time was running out for Martinsydes and he began to look around for alternative employment. This was a wise move for in 1922 Martinsydes folded as a company. Despite the diversification into motorcycles, the sudden loss of large military orders was too much for their limited resources and a receiver was appointed. The economic climate of the day was not conducive to the expensive task of designing, building and selling aeroplanes. However, Camm was kept on by the receiver to assist in clearing the limited assets of the company. This was a task which kept him employed for a few more months, until another opportunity beckoned.

In early 1922, shortly after Martinsydes collapsed, George Handasyde started a small aircraft design company and quickly obtained a contract to design a six-seat commercial high-wing monoplane for service in Australia. He had his old chief draughtsman, J.D. Stanbury, assisting him and they gladly took Camm on as a design assistant. The offices were in a wooden hut outside the Accumulator Works at Maybury Hill, Woking. Sydney and Hilda were still living conveniently close at West Byfleet.

Known as the Handasyde 'H2' the first, and only, example of this monoplane flew at Brooklands in December 1923 after construction by the Air Navigation & Engineering Company at its Addlestone Works. Whilst all this had been going on, Handasyde and Camm had in odd moments, managed to design a monoplane glider for the *Daily Mail*-sponsored trials due to be held at Itford, Sussex in October 1922. The winner was to be that which stayed airborne for the longest time.

Before all this happened and when they were still living at 18a Birchwood Road, West Byfleet, Hilda, in late 1921 announced she was pregnant, with an anticipated birth around next July. They had been married for nearly six years and the news of impending fatherhood must have excited Camm, despite the rather traumatic times as regards his employment. And so, on 10th July, 1922, a daughter, Phyllis, arrived safely at home. She was to be their only child. Camm must have been buried in his work and the forthcoming glider design, for it was not until 7th October that the birth was registered, and then Hilda had to manage that herself.

The glider was only finished the Wednesday before the start of the competition the following Monday. Camm accompanied it down to Itford where it was assembled and entered the trials, piloted by F.P. Raynham, showing great promise on the Sunday during its first test flights before the start of the competition. One noteable entry in this event was that of Anthony Fokker, the Dutch designer who brought a glider designed by himself and manufactured by his company in Holland. He put up some good steady times of around half-an-hour from the first day and the general opinion was that he could be the eventual winner. However, following a move along the Downs for

Where it all started for Camm as Chief Designer. The Canbury Road offices of the Sopwith Aviation company, before the renaming to Hawkers. *BAE Systems*

The design office at Canbury Park Road around 1927. Camm's office is the one that can be seen in the background. *BAE Systems*

a short distance suggested by Raynham, better gliding conditions were found and the next flight for the Handasyde/Camm entry, on Tuesday, was for 1 hour and 53 minutes, which placed it as the leader in the competition. They waited, pleased with this effort, for the nearest any others could make was just over half an hour, and were confident that their almost two hour glide would not be beaten. Until, on the Saturday, the last day of the trials, a Frenchman, Maneyrol, appeared at the last minute in his unorthodox tandem wing glider, and stayed airborne for over three hours, becoming the overall winner. However, Raynham was shortly afterwards awarded the Britannia Trophy for his record glide at this competition. This trophy had been created in 1913 by the Royal Aero Club from a prize offer by Mr H. Barber and was to be awarded annually for the most meritorious aviation performance of the year by a British aviator.

Shortly after this disappointment Camm was involved in the modification of an aircraft for the King's Cup Air Race, which in those early days was a two-day affair round Britain. This aircraft was a two-seat version of the Martinsyde 'F4' fitted with a 200 hp Hispano-Suiza engine, and the pilot F.P. Raynham of the glider episode. As much of the development work to get this aircraft ready had been done by Camm, it was natural for him to be asked by Raynham to go along on the actual race as the mechanic. They led the race after the long haul up to Renfrew in Scotland, despite the fact that they had a problem on the first leg to Birmingham. Here they found a broken water pipe on the engine and the cooling water drained away. Camm effected a temporary repair whilst the aircraft was refueled. This held for the remainder of the day's flying to Renfrew. They began the second day's return to London still in the lead for much of that day, but were overtaken by a 'DH4A' flown by Frank Barnard on the home leg, coming in second place just two minutes after him.

Camm's pilot friend Raynham also acted as a test pilot for the H.G. Hawker Engineering Company, which had been formed from the old Sopwith Aviation Company following bankruptcy caused by cancellation of large orders for fighter aircraft after the war had ended. Harry G. Hawker had been Tom Sopwith's test pilot throughout the war and, in that position, had had much say in the designs produced. Not wishing to see his old colleague's company disappear, Hawker gathered together a group of Sopwith Directors and refinanced the company, which resulted in the name change. Tragically, just eight months later he was killed in a test flight of a racing aircraft, the 'Nieuport Goshawk', at Hendon on 21st July, 1921. By this time Tom Sopwith had joined the Board and was elected Chairman in place of Hawker. One of his first decisions was to perpetuate Hawker's memory by keeping the company name. The aircraft work at that time was mainly concerned with rebuilding and modification of war surplus machines coming into the civil market.

The friendship of Camm and Raynham, bolstered by the King's Cup experience was, in the near future, to produce the catalyst for a job change. But before this, one more Handasyde episode was to happen.

The large public interest in the Itford gliding competition spurred the *Daily Mail* to sponsor a motor-glider competition in early 1923, Handasyde announced his intention of entering this, which was scheduled for October that year. He got down to designing the machine, much of the detail work being done by Camm,

Harry Hawker, Sopwith's test pilot, who was killed whilst testing a racing aircraft in 1921.
BAE Systems

but the small company was in no fit state to carry on much longer; money ran out and it was wound up. The motor-glider design, to be powered by a 750cc Douglas flat-twin engine, was built, but whether by Handasydes or elsewhere is not clear, and flown by F.P. Raynham just around the time of the collapse.

Camm was not out of a job for long, however, for following representation by Raynham, backed up by glowing testimonials from both Handasyde and Martin, he was offered the post of senior designer/draughtsman at the H.G. Hawker Engineering Company, then operating from Canbury Park Road, Kingston. This was by now an up and coming aircraft manufacturer, although small, and determined to get a firm foothold in the market for new fighter aircraft. The Chief Designer there was W.G. Carter, who had previously been chief draughtsman for the Sopwith Aviation Company. The Hawker concern, now established in the old Sopwith buildings in Kingston, was thus a small, but financially sound, company that Camm joined in November 1923. Here he was to stay until his death in 1966. Hawker's, following in the tradition of the Sopwith company, were to continue to specialize in the design and production of fighter aircraft as a main product, with sundry other types for light bombing or reconnaissance missions. In the fighter context, Camm's previous experiences at Martinsydes were to prove most useful in the near future.

In early 1924 Camm's first major design task for Hawker's descended on his drawing board from Carter. This was to get out the drawings of the Sopwith 'Tabloid' and design a modern version with half the power and half the weight. The 'Tabloid' of 1913 had an 80 hp engine and weighed roughly 1,100 pounds. So 40 hp and 550 pounds were his design criteria.

Using experience from his recent glider and motor-glider work with Handasyde, Camm drew the designs for the Hawker 'Cygnet'. Two aircraft were built and entered into the 1924 Lympne Light Aircraft Competition. A biplane of 28 ft span, it weighed empty just 411 lb., carried a pilot and passenger and was powered by a 34 hp engine, one being fitted with an Anzani and the other with an ABC Scorpion. The two entries, G-EBJH and G-EBMB came 3rd and 4th in the competition. The following year the 'Cygnet', flown by P.W.S. (George) Bulman, the chief test pilot for Hawker's, won the 100-mile International Handicap Race at Lympne. Shortly after this both the 'Cygnets' were re-engined with Bristol 'Cherub' 2-cylinder opposed engines and entered for the *Daily Mail* Light Aeroplane Competition, where they won the first two places.

The 'Cygnet' was a design masterpiece, Camm had got it right first time. His attention to the detail design ensured that the structural integrity was sound and the weight was well under control. His position at Hawker's was assured with this quality of work coming from him.

Then, in 1925, W.G. Carter had a disagreement with Fred Sigrist, one of the company's two Managing Directors and resigned his Chief Designer's position. Tom Sopwith, the other Managing Director then agreed with Sigrist that Camm be promoted into the vacant job. Carter was far from finished, he eventually became Chief Designer at Gloster Aircraft and was to make his name with the design of the Gloster 'E.28/39', the first British jet aircraft, followed by the first operational British jet fighter, the 'Meteor', in 1944. By that time Gloster's had been an independent subsidiary of Hawker's for nine years.

The Hawker 'Cygnet', Carmm's first design exercise at Hawkers. His success with this assured Tom Sopwith that Camm was a potential Chief Designer.   *BAE Systems*

To get from the shop floor to Chief Designer at the relatively young age of 32 had taken Camm just 11 years. He had proved himself in the 'Cygnet' design and stepped into his new responsibility as a new fighter design was being proposed. He already had some new ideas for metal structures, prompted by Sigrist and the Royal Air Force, both wanting to get rid of wood as a primary material. Up to now wood had been the prime structural medium, and with the new fighter prototype he began his efforts to win round a sometimes reluctant design team to his way of thinking, but his arguments were convincing, and so came into being the Hawker steel tube structure.

He had inherited a team of about 30 in the Design Office, which was adequate for the day, but as time progressed and the fortunes of Hawkers improved over the next two years this was to grow to about 40 as the workload increased. The current production was relatively steady and future prospects looked good with Hawker aircraft becoming popular with the RAF. There was considerable competition from other companies, however, particularly on the fighter front from the Bristol Aeroplane Company and Gloster Aircraft.

There has been a lot said about Camm's blunt approach to winning his team over. He had had to drive himself hard in his early days, probably aware that his working class upbringing clashed somewhat with the affluence of some of his aviation colleagues. To be Chief Designer he had to establish himself as the 'boss' in one of the most experienced aircraft design departments in the Country. He drove his team hard and had short shrift with any dissension over what he ordered. Intrinsically, he was a shy man, but when he made a point of insisting his way was right, this shyness evaporated and his attitude boiled over into what seemed at times an angry tirade. If an unfortunate draughtsman should not carry out what was ordered in the manner Camm expected, the ticking off was both public and instant, peppered with pointed comments and suitable expletives. Some of the more senior men tolerated this for but a short time and wrote to Tom Sopwith complaining about this attitude of Camm's. However, he survived this as there is no record of the response. Sopwith was astute enough to know by now that, given his way, Camm was usually right in his demands. The staff therefore learned to live with his outbursts, accepting it as a way of life with their forthright and fiery, but very competent, Chief Designer. He became known as Sydney to his team, but never to his face. (In later years this was changed to 'The Old Man' and after the knighthood it became 'Sir Syd'.) A perfectionist by nature where detail design was concerned, every drawing was personally checked before issue in the earlier years. As he integrated himself into this responsible position he always felt that both he and those under him owed a great deal to Tom Sopwith who took great interest in the designs under way, encouraging their efforts.

One little exercise carried out by Camm before his promotion was to draw up his idea as to what a possible monoplane fighter should look like. This was in 1925 and the original drawing, a three-view general arrangement, was signed by him. However, monoplanes were still not fashionable at that time and Sigrist and Carter showed little interest so the idea was not pursued any further. Camm's monoplane days were to come 10 years later, with the advent of the prototype 'Hurricane'.

As he consolidated his position as Chief Designer, Camm had the current design changes for the 'Horsley' day bomber to deal with. The 'Horsley' had entered production with a wood structure but external pressures from the Air Ministry, which had since 1926 pressed for such a change, were to alter this. Camm now had other plans so, wishing to introduce his own ideas on a metal structure, the aircraft was progressively redesigned until the final versions were primarily metal. In fact, the 'Horsley' changed during the production phase from its original wood structure to an early example of Camm's metal-structured aircraft. Powered by a Rolls-Royce 'Condor engine' of 665 hp, 130 'Horsleys' were to be built and delivered including six for the Greek Naval Air Service. Capable of carrying two 550 lb. bombs it entered service with 11 Squadron of the RAF in January 1927. This was a substantial order, the first for an aircraft employing Camm's metal structure concept which was to become standard for some considerable time. He always had placed great emphasis on weight control, largely through his involvements in designs where light weight was of paramount importance, so it was natural to carry this philosophy through to the future developments. Time and again, he would berate members of his team with the comment: 'I'll not 'ave it, what ever you say, it's too 'eavy!' Camm's aitches tended to become very sparse when he was worked up and making a point.

The first prototype fighter of Camm, the 'Heron', was a keynote design, for it brought in his ideas for metal construction of the main structure from the outset. For his fuselage he began scheming the employment of steel tubes joined

The big biplane built just before Camm was appointed Chief Designer. The Hawker 'Horsley' bomber towers over the figure standing beside it.

BAE Systems

A 'Horsley' displays its torpedo carrying ability. *Flight*

by steel brackets and plates using rivets and bolts which should, he reasoned, with internal wire bracing, produce a light and strong structure which was covered in fabric, suitably faired to streamline it. This was to continue right through the biplane fighters and onto the 'Hurricane' before the stressed skin structure became acceptable to Camm. His biplane wings employed steel spars and light alloy ribs again with internal bracing and fabric covering. The 'Heron' achieved a maximum speed of 156 mph at 9,800 ft. This placed it amongst the fastest fighters at the time.

With the 'Heron', Camm had set the style for his future series of biplanes. The wing layout and tail surface outlines would also be found in the 'Fury' fighter which was to come in 1929. After some service trials which resulted in considerable praise about the good handling characteristics and the ease of servicing obtained from the metal structure, it was eventually returned to Brooklands in May 1928. Despite its uncowled radial engine it was a neat-looking aircraft, but failed to attract any orders, which in those days were few and far between.

Although in his earlier days Camm had flown on test occasionally as a passenger when offered the chance, his airborne experiences by now were almost over. The first time he was known to fly in a Hawker aircraft with which he had much design involvement was in July 1925, not long after his attainment of the Chief Designer's job. He took a ride in the prototype 'Horsley' after it had been returned to Brooklands to have a redesigned undercarriage fitted. On landing a tyre burst causing the gear to collapse on one side and the aircraft

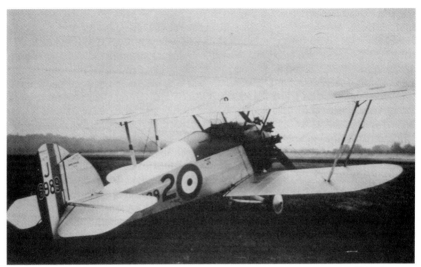

The Hawker 'Heron' of 1925.   *BAE Systems*

came to a shuddering halt on one wing and the surviving wheel. No injuries to
him or the pilot were recorded, but Camm never flew again on test and only
when absolutely necessary as a passenger. The latter was largely restricted to
flights to and from Paris to visit the air show. Further afield a brief North
American trip in the 1950s resulted in some short internal flights. Terra firma
was much more to his liking.

There were three intermediate aircraft designed and built as prototypes only
after the 'Horsley', these being the 'Hornbill', the 'Harrier' and the 'Hawfinch'.
Each were used as a means of improving the steel structure designs originally
used on the 'Heron'. The 'Hornbill', which had been a Carter design, employed
the first metal fuselage frame for Hawker's, but this was a welded frame.
Welding was never popular with Camm and he set about implementing his
own ideas as to how a metal fuselage might be constructed. This resulted in the
steel structural system described earlier, which would be the Hawker
trademark for nearly 15 years. He had put this idea to Sopwith and Sigrist, who
both immediately saw the production advantages in that this form of metal
structure could be built up anywhere in the factory without the need to provide
a specialist welding facility. Repair of damage to the aircraft would also be
easier and capable of being carried out in the field rather than the laborious task
of returning it to repair centres elsewhere.

Camm was always thinking of a slightly better way to apply his detail design
of the metal structures, until finally happy with the outcome which was then
covered by British patents 286482 and 292426 of 1927 for the fuselages, and
314131 of 1928 for the wing spars. These were taken out in the joint names of
Camm and Sigrist; the latter had been keen to support this new approach, for it

The Hawker 'Hornbill' of 1926.   *BAE Systems*

not only gave a stronger structure but proved to be easier and cheaper than the previous wooden structure to assemble on the production line.

Due to the fact that the 'Hornbill' had actually flown just as Camm was made Chief Designer, he had had little to do with the basic design. This aircraft had started the trend to break away from the current designs, which used air-cooled radial engines with the attendant drag penalty due to exposed cylinders (the NACA* cowl to remedy this was only still in the development stage then), and the new supercharged and liquid-cooled Rolls-Royce 'Condor III' engine had been selected to power it. Camm did, however, take much time in ensuring that the final design was as clean as possible in the search for speed.

Initial trials at Farnborough for the Air Staff were followed by time at the Aircraft and Armament Experimental Establishment, Martlesham Heath, where the RAF test pilots would appraise the aircraft's handling and performance. The top speed was approaching 185 mph but no decision as to a possible order resulted. In February 1926 the aircraft was returned to Hawkers at Brooklands, dismantled and taken to Kingston for modification. Camm, by now Chief Designer, carried out some design modifications, the major one being the fitting of a 'Condor IV' engine of 698 hp. This gave him the opportunity to redesign the engine cowling and change the cooling system to one employing a single radiator on the fuselage underside in place of the original two under-wing units. Thus modified, a level speed of 194 mph was achieved. However, the manoeuvre handling was not all that satisfactory and so the 'Hornbill' failed to attract an order. It did exhibit excellent low-speed handling characteristics and it ended its days on trials at Farnborough and Brooklands which studied the effects of automatic wing slats on handling near the stall speed.

---

* National Advisory Committee for Aeronautics (USA).

Also from the 'Hornbill', which had originally been designed by Carter, Camm took his engine-airframe layout which was to evolve into the classic 'Hart'/'Fury' shape. He was glad of the move to get rid of the draggy radial engine installation and replace this by blending the Rolls-Royce 'Condor' in-line engine arrangement into the front fuselage to achieve a more streamlined assembly. This had paid off in the achievement of the creditable top speed for the 'Hornbill'.

The next Hawker offering, the 'Harrier', designed to Specification 23/25, was not a successful aircraft. It was a large two-seat bomber/torpedo bomber powered by a Bristol 'Jupiter VIII' radial engine. It flew in February 1927 but was heavy with all the Ministry features required by the specification. With a torpedo weighing 2,800 lb., it failed to perform satisfactorily at its design weight of 5,656 lb. and Camm's comments, probably aimed at the Ministry, must have turned the air blue, to say the least. This was a classic example of 'Ministry modifications' which so often resulted in adverse effects on the performance of the aircraft in question.

However, one month later, the 'Hawfinch', a single-seat fighter design powered by a Bristol 'Jupiter VII' flew. It was in direct competition with the Bristol 'Bulldog' after the Boulton & Paul and Gloster entries had been eliminated at the trials held at Martlesham Heath. Despite the fact that the 'Bulldog' had to be modified to improve its spin recovery it was declared the winner after more trials later that year, on the grounds of better ease of maintenance. It also had a level speed of 178 mph as against 171 mph of the 'Hawfinch'. Camm complained bitterly that the 'Jupiter' engine supplied for the 'Hawfinch' was of inferior performance, but subsequent investigation of engine test records did not bear this out.

Out of the three unsuccessful types it was the 'Hornbill' which provided the basic in-line engine-fuselage combination for Camm to take as his baseline for future developments of what were to become his biplane masterpieces: the 'Hart' and 'Fury' designs, which were to dominate the scene for some years. Plus, of course, the new scheme for metal fuselage and wing construction.

Not long after Camm had risen to Chief Designer a new member had joined his team in the Design Office. This was Roy Chaplin who was taken on as assistant stressman in the early months of 1926. Camm soon realized that in Chaplin, who had a London University Honours Degree in engineering, he had a very competent stressman. Chaplin quickly picked up the aircraft design mantle with consummate ease and was always ready to pit his brains at various problems put his way now Camm was turning his mind to metal structures as a permanent feature for the future.

Chapter Three

Into the Thirties

In 1928 came the 'Hart', a keynote aircraft, one which was to sell in large numbers and confirm Camm's wisdom in going for his all-metal approach to basic structures combined with his keen eye for good aerodynamic shaping of the engine-fuselage assembly. On the subject of that art practised by Aerodynamists [sic], as he was wont to term them, his appreciation of smooth blended shapes for producing low aerodynamic drag was first class. The future aeroplanes were to be examples of how best to achieve that as typified by the 'Hart' fuselage, for the in-line engine variants anyway. In fact, a separate Aerodynamics Department never existed under Camm as that profession was alien to his way of thinking. So deep was this philosophy ingrained at Kingston that an Aerodynamics Department did not materialize until 1968, two years after his death, the work prior to that being carried out in the Project Office.

The prototype 'Hart' first flew in June 1928. Barely 15 months had elapsed since the first flight of the single-seat 'Hawfinch' fighter prototype, yet here was a two-seat light bomber which had excellent all-round performance, looked good and had excellent development potential. Other features which ensured its selection were, firstly, the top speed of 184 mph which was greater than all current in-service RAF fighters and was conferred by its Rolls-Royce 'Kestrel' engine of 525 hp. This new engine, which had been under development since 1924, together with its use in a range of Hawker aircraft during the 1930s, established Rolls-Royce's position as the premier supplier of aero engines to the RAF. Additionally, the range of the 'Hart' was a healthy 400 miles. With those attributes, after acceptance trials the 'Hart' was ordered into production.

One other vital feature of the 'Hart' design was the versatility which brought about the need to consider fitting other engines to meet other requirements. As enquiries built up for potential export orders, the Design Office was busy scheming the variants to meet the needs. Upwards of 10 variants per year was eventually the norm. Camm had his team right behind him and the enthusiasm he engendered saw them working all hours to produce the necessary drawings and schemes to answer the many problems which must have arisen.

With the advent of the 'Hart' and its many variants, three features of Camm's design philosophy stand out. These were, firstly an obsession for economy and, secondly, elegance; if it looked right it was much more likely to be right. (One of his favourite sayings, when questioned about the shapes he chose: was 'Handsome is as handsome does'.) Thirdly, no drawing would be issued unless the component was definitely minimum weight and unless the works could make that part with the machinery and skills available. In this latter context, if new tooling was required the case for manufacture had to be a cast-iron one. All this was fundamental to Camm's design approach at all times.

With the advent of his classic range of biplane fighters, light bombers and general purpose designs, Camm's reputation was secure. The Royal Aeronautical Society acknowledged this by elevating him to Fellowship level.

An aerial view of Brooklands, with an inverted 'Hart' trainer in the foreground.

The 'Hart' trainer prototype. Many of the existing 'Harts' were returned for conversion after the extended trials of the prototype resulted in an order for more. *BAE Systems*

An example of the first production (1929-1930) batch of the 'Hart' light bomber, J9941. *BAE Systems*

Two 'Harts' in formation, taken from another 'Hart'.   *BAE Systems*

A 'Hart' for the Latvian Air Force.   *BAE Systems*

He got the 'Hart' right from day one, which ensured its success. And so commenced an eight year production run, until over 3,000 of all versions had been built, many of them by other aircraft companies, as the Hawker production facilities could only cope with a little over half the numbers in that time.

It cannot be emphasized too much how important the 'Hart' basic design was to Hawker's. It set them up as the primary light bomber supplier to the RAF in the early 1930s. The basic design was also used as an engine test-bed from 1930 onwards for the Rolls-Royce 'Kestrel', 'PV12' and 'Merlin' developments of in-line liquid-cooled engines, the Bristol 'Jupiter', 'Pegasus', 'Mercury' and 'Perseus' air-cooled radials, plus the Napier 'Dagger', Hispano-Suiza '12' and Lorraine 'Petrel'. The American Pratt & Whitney 'Hornet' and French Gnome-Rhone also appeared on export versions.

According to those that flew it, the 'Hart' was a reliable, trouble-free aircraft with no vices and good handling qualities. Some of the exported examples, in particular those supplied to the Afghan Air Force, lasted into the 1950s before final withdrawal from service.

It was also a great example of how to produce a range of aircraft for different roles using a common basic design. Derivatives could be produced quickly and at low cost due to common tooling, components and existing constructional techniques. The first major derivative was the 'Demon', a two-seat fighter, which took advantage of the excellent level speed of the 'Hart'. Over 300 were ordered, 64 of which went to the Royal Australian Air Force. One interesting batch of 10 for the RAF had a power-operated gun turret fitted, brought about by the extreme difficulties experienced by the gunner in sighting his gun in an airstream exceeding 200 mph. This proved quite successful and many other 'Demons' were retrospectively modified.

Then came the 'Audax', a close-support version to specification 7/31 for home service and later, specification 19/34 for overseas service. Nearly 550 were produced for these specifications. The 'Audax' also spawned two sub-types, the 'Hardy', 47 built for service in the Middle East, and the 'Hartbee' for South Africa, 69 built, 65 of them under licence in South Africa.

The Navy also had a requirement O.22/26 for a fleet spotter/reconnaisance aircraft for which the 'Hart' was tendered, and after the 'Hart' prototype had been altered to meet this specification it was put forward and obtained a small production contract. The main modifications were folding wings, a strengthened structure to permit catapult launching plus the ability to fit floats for operation from capital ships such as cruisers or battleships with catapult facilities. Over 100 were eventually ordered by the Royal Navy, being given the name 'Osprey'. One batch of six were built using stainless steel in place of the aluminium and steel original structure, but no production change was incorporated after this. As a point of interest, all Hawker aircraft fitted with floats had those items supplied by Short Brothers.

The final two derivatives were firstly, the 'Hind' which was basically an update of the 'Hart' required to keep the light bomber squadrons up to strength until the Bristol 'Blenheim' and Fairey 'Battle' types came into service. Over 500 'Hinds' were produced with about 50 going to other countries. Secondly, the

The Hawker 'Audax' army co-operation biplane. This is the preserved example of the
Shuttleworth Collection, rescued from Afghanistan in 1970, on display at Horse Guards Parade.
Note the 'Hurricane' and Supermarine 'S6B' in the background.   *Unknown source*

The 'Osprey', a naval version of the 'Hart', for fleet spotting and reconnaissance.
                                                                        BAE Systems

The Hawker 'Hind', an updated version of the 'Hart' to supplement those already in service since 1929. *BAE Systems*

A 'Hind' for the Yugoslav Air Force. *BAE Systems*

Portugal bought some 'Hinds' as well, this being one of them.   *BAE Systems*

The 'Hinds' supplied to Persia differed from the standard design in having radial engines (Bristol 'Mercury VIII').   *BAE Systems*

Hawker 'Hector' Army co-operation biplane of 1935, the last biplane design to come from Camm, as the monoplane 'Hurricane' was by now top priority.   *Flight*

'Hector' which was basically to replace or supplement some of the early 'Audax' used for army co-operation. The 'Hector', of which 178 were built, was unique in that it was designed for the Napier 'Dagger III' engine. This was because the 'Hind' production required most of the available Rolls-Royce 'Kestrel' production.

However, as the 1930s opened, there was another key design coming along at this time, which was to become Camm's classic single-seat biplane fighter, the 'Fury'.

With the 'Fury', designed to Ministry specification F.13/30, the 200 mph-plus fighter appeared for the first time. As a matter of fact, the specification hinted quite strongly that a monoplane might be the best answer in the quest for high performance. Camm thought otherwise at this point and the 'Hart' influence was there for all to see in the beautifully blended engine and fuselage integration. It was, perhaps, the best looking biplane fighter ever produced and a classic example of Camm's design expertise. The cooling of the 'Kestrel' was enhanced by the provision of a new ducted radiator under the fuselage. This lowered the drag and with an improved propeller, produced the maximum speed increase to enable the 200 mph to be exceeded at last. In fact, development of the 'Fury' was to raise its level speed to 240 mph by the early 1930s. They were also to become regular participants at the Hendon air displays in the 1930s with their aerobatic prowess and formation fly-pasts. It became a main front-line day fighter for the RAF alongside the 'Bulldog' and 'Siskin III' but as the 1930s marched on and German rearmament became more assertive, the day of the biplane was to come to an end for such use.

Eight 'Furys' in echelon left formation.   *BAE Systems*

The 'Fury' biplane fighter K1944 of the first production batch of 1931.   *BAE Systems*

'Fury' biplane fighter at Brooklands, *c*.1931.   *BAE Systems*

Biplane 'Fury' K1944 climbs away.   *BAE Systems*

The Hawker 'Tomtit' training biplane of 1929. This one is G-AFTA when in the ownership of
Neville Duke (in rear cockpit).   *BAE Systems*

The 'Fury' had two main derivatives, the first being the 'Nimrod' Naval fighter, to specification 16/30. Fifty-six were built, some with modifications to enable them to be operated on floats when required. They replaced the dated Fairey 'Flycatchers' on the carriers *Courageous, Furious* and *Glorious*. The second was the single prototype of the high-speed 'Fury'. This was built as a private venture in order to test a range of Rolls-Royce engines, four 'Kestrel' variants and two marks of the evaporative-cooled 'Goshawk'. Two sets of upper wings were provided, one of which incorporated the steam condensers for the 'Goshawk' installation. Immediately before the first flight the Air Ministry placed it on an experimental charge, thus the construction and engine tests were covered at the Ministry's expense with the aircraft accumulating some 800 hours flying over a three year period, ending in 1936.

One design to depart from the range of light bombers and fighters being developed was the 'Tomtit' basic trainer of 1928. Conceived as an *ab initio* trainer to replace the by now obsolete Avro '504s', which still soldiered on after 14 years' service, the 'Tomtit' came at a time when output of 'Harts' and 'Furys' took practically all the Hawker's available factory space. What had instigated the design was a Ministry remark that it was time that a metal basic trainer should be available (the '504' was all-wooden construction), which Camm took up as a project for his team. A prototype was built as a private venture and flew in November 1928. Production, after service trials, only reached a total of 28 aircraft and, although the RAF took a production batch of 10, competition from other manufacturers made it a non-starter as a basic trainer for the Royal Air Force. The flying qualities were, according to some pilots, ideal for basic training and it was also fitted with the newly-developed Reid and Sigrist blind flying equipment. Sales of the civil variant never got under way sufficiently to warrant a more aggressive marketing stance. Hawker's were, after all, primarily suppliers of military aircraft.

There had been a feeling abroad in political circles and elsewhere that, 'the bomber will always get through' and that spending money on fighter aircraft was a waste, so little funding was available from Ministry sources. However, Air Marshal Sir Hugh Dowding had other ideas and wished to build up an effective fighter force for the defence of the country. In 1930 the Air Ministry bowed to his pressure and issued Specification F.7/30 which included the following requirements:

a   A low landing speed and short landing run
b   A maximum speed of 250 mph
c   A steep initial climb for interception
d   High manoeuvrability
e   Good all-round view

This specification was put out to the British aircraft industry and from the many submissions prototype contracts were given to the Blackburn, Westland and Supermarine companies. Bristol's and Hawker's were also encouraged to produce private venture solutions. Out of these, Bristol and Supermarine put forward monoplane designs, the Bristol one incorporating a retractable undercarriage, so in that respect, a trend had been set. However, the design studies spread into 1933, by which time the RAF announced that trials would not be held until the following year. Then the British Intelligence sources, backed up by observations of some aviation people who had been fortunate enough to briefly view the resurgent German aircraft factories whilst looking for new civil aircraft, soon realized that the new generation of German airliners would easily turn into bombers and, with the speeds being quoted, would easily outrun the current British biplane fighters. Reports to this effect began filtering through to Hawker's. A challenge was appearing and the Hawker management took it up.

Also, in early 1934, Rolls-Royce ordered from the German Heinkel company an example of their new monoplane, the 'He70', stipulating that it be powered by its 'Kestrel' engine. A 'Kestrel' was shipped over to Germany and, whilst it waited to be installed in the Heinkel, was used for the maiden flights of two key aircraft to appear in the Luftwaffe inventory, the 'Ju87' 'Stuka' and the Messerschmitt 'Bf109'. Then, when the Heinkel was ready, the potential of the monoplane was shown by the 260 mph level speed reached with six people on board.

Clearly, this meant that the Germans would have bombers capable of speeds up to, and maybe beyond, the 260 mph of the Heinkel. This fact hit home in Britain and once Camm heard of that potential he immediately set his sights on bettering the requirements of 'F.7/30', which was now most certainly out-of-date.

We have already seen that Camm had proposed a monoplane some seven years previously, but then they were not fashionable and the suggestion died. Sigrist still held a strong influence over what the Design Office was to offer in the way of new projects. Camm had agreed with him in respect of the introduction of the metal structure and, indeed, as we have seen, Sigrist was co-patentee of that. However, there still remained some matters of the manufacturing techniques. Sigrist was against anything which would bring in new skills and methods as they might be liable to increase costs and call for expensive new tooling. All-metal monocoque construction methods were coming along and threatened the status quo and there was a constraint to keep to established methods as then in use at Hawker's. However, the revelations from Germany in terms of the rearmament programme and the types of aircraft now being developed gave Camm a good argument in favour of the monoplane approach at least. How he managed to design the next fighter is a classic example of brilliant compromise enabling the final 'Fury' aircraft, to become the 'Hurricane', to be an easily produced and highly effective interceptor fighter. The structure, particularly that of the fuselage, although thought dated by some, was to show surprisingly good tolerance to battle damage plus ease of repair when damaged.

In the summer of 1933 a significant event took place, this being the renaming of the company, from the H.G. Hawker Engineering Company to that of Hawker Aircraft Limited, which was incorporated as a public company. As the years progressed the renamed company was to become the catalyst for a great aircraft engineering consortium. Camm and his team therefore marched forward into the new era of the modern monoplane with its enclosed cockpit, retractable undercarriage and multi-gun armament as the first great product to come from the rejuvenated company.

Chapter Four

The 'Hurricane'

Camm knew that to improve fighter speeds the way would have to be via the low drag monoplane with a fully enclosed cockpit and, in late 1933, ordered the Drawing Office to scheme what was initially known as the 'Fury Monoplane'. On 5th December, 1933, the general arrangement drawing was issued for discussion purposes. Up to now, most fighters had been fitted with just two machine guns firing through the propeller. The specification then current called for four guns, and the 'Fury' monoplane was intended to have that number, two in the wing roots and two fuselage mounted.

This first iteration employed the 'Fury' fuselage shape with a cockpit hood and fairing, a new cantilever tapered wing was planned and the airframe was intended to take the new Rolls-Royce 'Goshawk' in-line engine. This engine was a development of the 'Kestrel' but had an unorthodox evaporative cooling system. The cooling medium was water, which would have to be condensed from the steam produced by its cooling the engine in radiators placed in the wing leading edge. In retrospect, this seems a very unsafe way to achieve the cooling, as battle damage to the wings could lead to leakage of the cooling water which would cause overheating and consequent seizure of the engine. However, events concerning the cooling system were to eliminate this power-plant. The undercarriage, which remained fixed, was fitted with streamlined spats. However, the performance did come up to that thought necessary for an effective fighter/pursuit machine. The current thinking in the specifications indicated that 275 mph would be the target.

Up to now Camm had been against a retractable undercarriage on the grounds of expense and weight, but the performance advantages plus a change of policy on the engine were to change his position. The development of the 'Goshawk' was discontinued as Rolls-Royce had encountered severe problems with the cooling system. To replace it came the 'PV12', a larger, more powerful development of the 'Kestrel'. This engine, to become the 'Merlin', offering 1,025 bhp at 2,900 rpm and 15,000 feet altitude, is often thought as being derived from the Rolls-Royce 'R' developed for the Vickers-Supermarine entry which won the Schneider Trophy outright in 1931. However, it was a new design as depicted by its designation, 'PV12' (Private Venture 12-cylinder). It had a Glycol cooling system with the fluid being cooled in a single radiator mounted under the fuselage. The elimination of the wing leading edge radiator and associated pipes required by the now defunct 'Goshawk' engine meant that there was more space in the wings available for a retractable undercarriage.

The crucial matter in fighter development beyond the 'Fury' was that of a monoplane layout. Biplanes, whilst light and strong structurally when assembled, had a structural assembly which kept manufacturing techniques at an affordable cost. Selling price being a key factor in obtaining orders at that time, the production techniques were more or less fixed until a more radical approach appeared at a reasonable cost.

Prototype monoplane 'Fury' LA610.   *BAE Systems*

Camm therefore decided to stay with the all-metal basic structure approach so successfully developed for the 'Hart'/'Fury' line. This constrained him to go initially for fabric covering on the wings, a matter which, we shall see, soon changed. The fuselage, whilst metal skinned, but unstressed, as far back as the cockpit, remained fabric covered for the rear portion as on the biplanes. His compromise placated those who were, initially, skeptical about monoplanes whilst ensuring that the skills and techniques available in the shops could be employed to full advantage.

One little idiosyncrasy of Camm was his view on days lost due to sickness. Days lost were crucial, it disrupted the flow of work. He would sometimes complain loud and long that no one had a right to be ill.

Then, in the middle of all the furore over the redesign of the 'Interceptor' monoplane, as the project was now called, one day he failed to turn up for work. No immediate explanation was forthcoming until later that day the news filtered through that he had been taken to hospital with appendicitis. This turned into peritonitis and resulted in his being absent for over six weeks.

There was, however, one benefit from Camm's absence, this being the deletion of the 'Hurricane' tailplane struts. Chaplin had stressed the tailplane and was confident that the struts were not necessary. He accordingly, acting as Camm's deputy, ordered their deletion on the final production drawings.

Whether or not the previous few months of ever-changing workload and priorities had had some bearing on Camm's health is a matter for speculation, but his seemingly iron constitution could well have been eroded by the never-ending responsibilities thrust upon him and precipitated his illness. However, his team carried on minus his guidance and little time was lost. The only problem that they had was fighting off sundry suggestions by George Bulman (chief test pilot) on some aspects of the design, which they reckoned would inflame Camm on his return.

When the major design changes of retractable undercarriage and a new engine were decided, it was March 1934. By June of that year the design was more or less frozen and a one-tenth scale model had been made for testing in the National Physical Laboratory (NPL) compressed air wind tunnel. The wing of this model, being machined from solid duralumin, had to be manufactured at Rolls-Royce, who had the necessary machine shop facilities. The testing commenced in August, confirming that the layout as chosen was satisfactory with no untoward effects at the speeds covered. The drawings of the fuselage were released in October and the structural design of the wing, which had to be new from the outset, was well under way.

The wind tunnel tests soon produced enough data for some meaningful performance predictions to be made. These resulted in the estimated level speed being confirmed as 320 mph at 16,000 ft as predicted earlier. So the 300 mph barrier should now be breached by a fighter aircraft, a quantum leap from the 200 mph-plus of the 'Fury'. The monoplane layout, combined with a retractable undercarriage and the 1,025 bhp 'PV12' engine had done the trick. Had it not been for Camm's skillful handling of the design process and insisting that the management should follow his road, the final outcome might have been very different. Hawker's now had a future front-line fighter on the drawing board, a

Prototype 'Fury' monoplane 'Fury' LA610. This had a Napier 'Sabre VII' engine which gave it a top speed of 485 mph, the fastest of all Camm's piston-engined fighters. *BAE Systems*

Prototype monoplane 'Fury' LA610. *BAE Systems*

prototype being contemplated and future production, in some quantity, was within reach. The Board had a challenge ahead in the implementation of all this.

Matters concerning the Government of the day took a jump forward in July of that year. On 23rd July a debate in Parliament had resulted from the statement that the Royal Air Force was to be increased by 41 squadrons over the next five years from the current 42 Home Defence squadrons, or 488 front-line aircraft. After a week of hot debate the vote was taken which enabled this enlargement programme to be commenced. And so the politicians began to wake from their lethargy.

However, as yet no formal contract had been received by Hawker's from the Ministry and with the wind-tunnel testing complete the construction of a wooden mock-up began. Technical staff levels had also risen, with 100 being available by the end of 1934. Camm, realizing that the work to turn a project study into hardware was going to be considerable, made sure that sufficient experienced people were recruited to cope with the needs. He also wanted a few members of his team to involve themselves in project work for future designs, for it was obvious by now that the 'Hurricane' would need a successor at some time in the near future.

The matter of the lack of wind tunnel facilities needs some qualification here. Hawker's, whilst Camm was there and, in fact for the whole of their existence at Kingston, never had their own wind tunnels. The National Physical Laboratory at Teddington provided such facilities as were needed in the 1930s during the 'Hurricane' development. In later years Camm had a good rapport with the Royal Aircraft Establishment (RAE) at Farnborough whose Miss Bradfield arranged many wind tunnel tests there for Hawker's. These seem never to have been charged for, the RAE absorbing the cost as part of their research programme. Camm was always to put much reliance on Miss Bradfield's analysis of any new design being tested at Farnborough.

On 2nd August, 1934, the Board of Rolls-Royce took the decision to contribute the sum of £5,000 towards the cost of building the 'Hurricane' prototype. The company clearly had great confidence in Camm's design abilities to place such a sum at the disposal of Hawker's plus, of course, a view as to future sales. Tom Sopwith replied to thank Rolls-Royce for this generous offer, and expressed his appreciation for the spirit in which it was made.

Through all this relations with the Air Ministry had been good, with each new idea, if useful, being applied to the steady iterations coming from the Design Office. These, as they appeared were put to the Ministry along with the relevant three-view drawings. Around these the Ministry would draw up a new specification so the design of the 'Interceptor' monoplane was virtually firmed up into a final prototype standard, the Air Ministry placing an order for the prototype on 20th September, 1934, only 16 days after a similar order to Supermarine's for the 'Spitfire' prototype. The company current specification had become F.36/34 in August 1934. This document was to be the datum specification one for the prototype.

In January 1935, not long after his return to work following his illness, Camm and his senior staff, together with the Air Ministry representatives, held a crucial meeting, with the mock-up providing much of the matters to be talked

The prototype 'Hurricane' with wooden fixed pitch propeller c.1937.

BAE Systems

over. One result of these discussions was a re-estimate of the normal loaded weight of 4,900 lb., a fact which Camm clearly resented but realized as being inevitable at this stage. He could do little to offset the weight growth, particularly as by now, the requirement to fit eight machine guns was firm.

Then, in February 1935, the long-awaited contract for one high speed monoplane arrived. The Ministry also had it listed as the single-seat fighter to specification F.36/34. The aircraft serial number allocated was K5083. The prototype was, by agreement with the Ministry, not to have the guns installed, this being covered later that year by an amendment to the contract which covered the production of a second set of outer wings incorporating the eight machine guns.

The next few months were ones of great activity in the Design Office (DO) and Experimental Department, where the prototype was now taking shape. Camm had, by this time, put a section of the Drawing Office upstairs as the Experimental DO which from now on would deal with all new projects. Any overload on their part would be dealt with in the original DO. This reorganization was in force when in August 1936 the whole design Department was moved out of its rather cramped offices and relocated in a building across Canbury Park Road, known as the 'old' furniture depository. This had been acquired the previous year to relieve the increasingly cramped conditions on the original site. The top floor of this building accommodated the Design Offices, the ground floor being used as stores for the plant across the road. Needless to say, Camm relocated with the Design Office, thus keeping a good eye on the matters needing his attention and approval. This relocation was also convenient for the experimental shop, where the prototype 'Hurricane' was to take shape, which was located in the next-door building.

Whilst all the above was happening at Kingston, Rolls-Royce had not been idle on the 'PV12' engine. It so happened that shortly before the events at Kingston mentioned above Rolls-Royce had set up a small flight test facility at Hucknall. This consisted of one hangar and a staff of 25. In the hangar were a Hawker 'Hart' and 'Fury' plus a Gloster 'Gnatsnapper'. It was here, on 12th April, 1935, that the 'PV12' engine took to the air for the first time in the 'Hart'. The first 60 hours flying were spent in perfecting the cooling system, for there were some early problems with it, whilst back at the Derby factory other engines were being prepared for Hawker's.

The 'PV12' was to be a key engine in the Rolls-Royce output, this was obvious at the start, for not only had it been selected for the Hawker fighter, but the Supermarine fighter proposal, to become the 'Spitfire' and the Fairey light bomber project, the 'Battle'. So if all three aircraft were to go into production, and they did, prospects were good. This spurred Rolls-Royce to place a good effort behind any problems occurring during the engine's development. Initially, all these applications employed a fixed-pitch propeller. Variable pitch propellers were still at the development stage, and were to come as a retrofit later.

Back at Kingston, the big task allotted the Design Office was the completely new wing for the monoplane. Initially to be designed as a fabric-covered structure, it was a new structural concept from the beginning for Hawker's. The centre-section was attached permanently to the fuselage and the outer wings were built as separate units. The fabric covering was to be a temporary measure only, but it got the wings to the production stage much earlier than if a metal covered stressed-skin structure had been decided upon. This latter change took place once production was under way, the structural design of the initial wing being given to stressman P.B. Walker. He had joined the company in January 1933 and was soon given the task of stressing the wing. In those days the mathematical problems of stressing such a structure as was proposed were considerable. The task was taken up by Walker and he was able to determine that whilst there was adequate strength for the loading anticipated, problems could be present at very high speeds which would produce some high torsional (twisting) loads due to the aerodynamic forces at very high speeds. The fabric covering would not be able to resist these loads so it would be necessary to resort to a metal skin. This was then adopted as a key feature for the definitive design which actually was in service as war broke out. The first batches of aircraft used the current Hawker fabric-covered metal wing concept suitably strengthened to combat the anticipated torsional loads inherent with a cantilever wing up to a lower limiting speed than would be acceptable for a metal-skinned version. The biplane layouts up to now had provided a stiff structure due to the bracing wires resisting torsional loads.

However, some of the Mk I 'Hurricanes' sent to France in the early days of the war actually did have the fabric wings and the fixed pitch propeller, but progressive refits of both items had eliminated them well before the Battle of Britain.

Walker, in fact was to leave Hawker's at the end of 1935 and by 1945 had become Head of Structures at the Royal Aircraft Establishment, Farnborough. So Camm's choice was a good one at a critical time and enabled the production of the necessary data to enable him to argue successfully for the change to a metal-skinned wing.

Whilst on the subject of delegation, Camm often let his staff use their initiative and originality. A stressman from his team standing by a draughtsman's board deep in discussion would not be castigated for time wasting, for out of that discussion might come an idea to solve a problem. However, anyone from another department would immediately be thrown out. Press his team hard for the answers he might, but he had gone through that process himself in the past and knew from hard experience that a team given their way would mould into a good design organization. Also encouraged was the opportunity to go down to the workshops to keep in touch with production matters concerning the current designs. In general, despite his sometimes withering outbursts, the atmosphere in the Design Office was a good relaxed one, which contributed towards the company's success.

With the fortunes of Hawker's boding well, Tom Sopwith saw to it that other aircraft companies benefited from production contracts to fulfill Hawker's delivery schedules. He also did not wish to see those companies formed by his old pioneering colleagues from the early days at Brooklands going into bankruptcy for lack of orders and made plans for the future acquisition of Armstrong Whitworth and A.V. Roe in particular. We shall see later how this materialized. There was an ulterior motive in these moves, as Sopwith wished to build up his company for the future. There was sense in all this, for a large concern would be able to manage large contracts much better under one roof, so to speak. And so the growth of Hawker's to the Hawker Siddeley Group began. With Hawker Aircraft now a public company with some £2 million capital from the share issue, it was positioned well for expansion and this began in February 1934 with the purchase of the Gloster Aircraft Company which was producing the 'Gauntlet' fighter in quantity and currently testing the 'Gladiator' which was soon to get some production orders. The Gloster aircraft production facility at Hucclecote was one of the largest such concerns in the country.

Sopwith wisely made no attempt to integrate or disband the design teams at the other companies absorbed into the Hawker Siddeley empire. Competition was good for all the teams and some companies, for instance Avro, were better suited to the design of larger multi-engined aircraft. An example of this appeared in 1937 when the specification P.13/36 for a medium bomber was issued. Hawker's at Kingston submitted their design for this, as did Avro. Both submissions were powered by two Rolls-Royce 'Vultures'. The Avro design won and was ordered, becoming the 'Manchester', which entered service in 1941 only to be withdrawn within a few months due to the continued failures of the 'Vulture' engines. The design was revamped with a new wing and four 'Merlins' to become the 'Lancaster', one of the most effective heavy bombers of the war.

In June 1935, the Hawker company added some new Directors to its Board, with Sydney Camm, George Bulman, H. Chandler, H.K. Jones and R.W. Sutton the chosen officers. His appointment to the Board made no difference to the way in which the Design Office was run, Camm stayed fully in command, but had the advantage of direct access within the Board on all matters.

For a Chief Designer to reach the Boardroom was a rare event, but this appointment showed how highly Camm was regarded by the company management. For it was largely his handling of the design of a range of successful aircraft which had been ordered in quantity that had put Hawker's into a commanding position in the British aircraft industry of the day. Sopwith was an astute businessman and, although in later years he accredited his success leading to the opportunity to form the Hawker Siddeley Group as 'pure luck', it really was the strong position that was obtained by Camm-designed aircraft that produced the means of launching his enterprise. That really was a key reason why Sydney Camm was made a Director. His arrival in the Boardroom would also have injected some forthright comments on policy affecting design matters.

Later in 1935, as events in Germany began to present a threat, all mention of international disarmament disappeared from the political scene except for a few head-in-the-sand pacifist-inclined MPs. Also the Air Estimates for that year were increased from the previous year's £7 million to £11 million. A large proportion of this increase was to come to Hawker's and Sopwith continued his growth plans. Firstly he formed a trust which was to acquire all the shares of the Armstrong Siddeley Development Company Ltd. Whilst the Hawker/Gloster combination put half its share capital in the Hawker Siddeley company, the rest

T.O.M. Sopwith *c*.1940.

BAE Systems

was retained to enable Hawker's to keep a degree of autonomy with one million pounds capital behind it.

The Armstrong Siddeley concern brought four companies of considerable size and influence into the merged concern: Sir W.G. Armstrong Whitworth Aircraft Ltd, Armstrong Siddeley Motors Ltd, Air Service Training Ltd and A.V. Roe & Company Ltd. The Hawker Siddeley Group, as it was eventually known, was to expand further in future years, absorbing de Havillands, Blackburn Aircraft and Folland Aircraft plus other ancillary companies. Sopwith had spent much time planning all this and the standing of Hawker's obtained by the success of Camm's designs played a great part in the achievement of this industrial empire.

The parallel development of the industrial complex by Sopwith with the advent of the 'Hurricane' and the political awakening to counter Germany's threat is a classic example of an astute businessman placing his industrial muscle behind the awakening Government. The timing was absolutely correct, any delay from the actual dates would have left the country at a severe disadvantage in 1939.

With the vastly-increased capital available from the new company, Hawker's started making plans for quantity production of the new fighter. The immediate question was, where was this production to be? The Canbury Park Road site certainly could not cope with the rate of production envisaged, so plans were made in early 1935 to erect extra production facilities at Brooklands. The site chosen was that originally used by the flying sheds of the old pioneers in pre-war days. This was opposite the Hawker flight sheds, not far from where the Marks & Spencer/Tesco shopping complex stands today.

Through all this reorganization the design of the 'Hurricane' continued on and production drawings were released as available to the Experimental and Production shops. The 'PV12' engine arrived from Rolls-Royce in the Autumn of 1935 and by 23rd October the construction of the prototype was complete and it was ready for transfer to Brooklands, where it was assembled and prepared for engine ground runs. On 6th November all was ready for the first flight. Camm drove over from Kingston that day and George Bulman prepared for a momentous occasion. It was just 11 months since the issue of the first drawings.

Once all the pre-flight checks had been carried out Bulman started the engine and taxied out for take-off. He lined up at the end of the grass runway, opened the throttle and the roar of the 'PV12', soon to become the 'Merlin', shattered the peace. The 'Hurricane' sped along the ground and lifted into the air gracefully to climb away. Bulman kept the undercarriage down for this first assessment and contented himself with a general look at the handling qualities as he made several circuits of the airfield. After satisfying himself that all was well he banked round for the landing approach. The landing itself was a short one following a surprisingly slow approach. He taxied back to where Camm and others were standing and switched off the engine. Sydney Camm clambered onto the wing root and looked quizzically at George Bulman sitting in the cockpit. Bulman turned to him and spoke 'Another winner, I think'.

Thus the story of the Hawker 'Hurricane' began, an aircraft that was to run to 14,500 examples of seven major variants over a 10-year span. An aircraft which

111 Squadron 'Hurricanes' in formation, *c*.1938. *BAE Systems*

would be a fighter, fighter-bomber and even Naval fighter and was to make its mark permanently in the history of the aerial warfare of World War II.

As all the development work on the 'Hurricane' proceeded, the works continued to turn out the biplanes, the RAF taking some, but with several batches going for export. By 1937 85 per cent of the Royal Air Force's strength were Hawker machines. To achieve that enviable figure much contracting out had been necessary and Camm was recorded as saying: 'We had over half the British aircraft industry building our designs'. But, by this time, Hawker's had virtual control over most of the half referred to.

By this time, the Camms were living in Thames Ditton just a few miles from the design offices. The house 'Carradale' was a substantial one, as befits a company Director, with a large garden and garage.

Chapter Five

The Approach of War

By now the clouds of war were rolling ever nearer, with the accelerated German rearmament taking place, and the British Government at last beginning to take action to prepare for conflict, albeit slowly. The Air Estimates were further increased in 1936 and Hawker's started preparations for expanding their production facilities. In December 1934 the German air force strength had been 1,888 aircraft of which 584 were operational front line types. By 1936 these numbers would have risen considerably, for the production rate of all types was estimated to be 160 aircraft per month. These figures did not go unnoticed by those interested in keeping our air force in a state whereby it could respond to such a threat posed by a large modern air force.

The Hawker Board was expecting a sizeable order for the 'Hurricane', in the region of 600 aircraft, following the completion of trials at Martlesham Heath. By now, the first wings fitted with the eight-gun installation were available and showed a devastating fire-power. And with a top speed of 330 mph the 'Hurricane' was a match for any known fighter of the day. The Hawker Board thought that the initial order of 600 was too little and would inhibit the RAF's response, particularly if losses were high.

German forces reoccupied the Rhineland on 7th March, 1936. This provocative move was noted by the British and French Governments which seemed unable to act in unison or accord, with the result that apart from some stern comments to German ambassadors, no action was taken to reverse the occupation. However, the Board of Hawker's thought that they had a duty to play some concrete part in preparing the country for war and at their March meeting made the decision to start production before the receipt of the Ministry contract. Although the official order was some months away it was decided that the company would tool up and order the supply of materials for 1,000 aircraft. Any delay in waiting for the order could be crucial in ensuring the RAF had sufficient stocks to cover losses. The 'Hurricane' production thus started at Hawker's expense, such was the threat of war interpreted by the Board.

Whilst the 'Hurricane' was being put into production, Camm had the Design Office busy, firstly on the design of an all-metal wing, the original fabric-covered one already considered obsolete, caused by the limitation put on the maximum dive speed. New fastenings to hold the fabric firmly in place at the much higher speeds had already been developed but, as mentioned earlier, it was the torsional strength of the wing that was the limiting factor. A metal-skinned wing would have a much higher dive speed limit. Camm had a first class stressman in P.B. Walker, who was given the task, which involved redesigned spars and ribs, with the internal structural layout considerably changed from that of the original wing. However, the initial production batches were to be delivered with the fabric wings until the new metal wing was in quantity production, despite the limit put on the diving speed, which was 80 mph less than that available with the metal wing.

'Hurricane' production under way at Langley.

BAE Systems

This was not the only significant early change concerning the 'Hurricane', for following the decision to go ahead, should orders go beyond the 1,000 mark, to increase output a new factory would be needed. That the production was going to exceed 1,000 was, by now, a foregone conclusion.

During all the efforts to get the 'Hurricane' to the production stage, another successful contender for F.36/34 was being built, the 'Spitfire'. The Supermarine design team, under Reginald Mitchell, had ploughed all their efforts into this new fighter. In fact the prototype ordered had been given its serial number K5036 much earlier than the 'Hurricane's' K5054, in keeping with the prototype order. But being an all-metal stressed skin structure, the tooling for production was taking a considerable time to organize. The shape of the 'Spitfire' was such that much double curvature on panels abounded and considerable effort was being expended in productionizing this. For although Supermarine had designed and built the metal-structured Schneider Trophy seaplanes these had only been prototypes. This slowed things down somewhat, and although an order for 310 aircraft was to be placed once the prototype had been assessed, the management of Supermarine's did not launch out in the manner of Hawker's and appeared to prefer to wait for the official order to come through. That is why the 'Spitfires' were only really available in sufficient quantity in mid-1940, just in time for the Battle of Britain.

It seems improbable that Hawker's knew of the potential competition from the Supermarine proposal when starting their design studies leading to the 'Hurricane'. Camm knew that his best chance in obtaining an order for his proposal lay in developing a design which, whilst giving the required performance, would be quick and easy to produce. This meant that, where possible, existing structural techniques and production methods would need to be followed.

The companion to the 'Hurricane' in the Battle of Britain, the 'Spitfire'.   *BAE Systems*

In adopting this philosophy, Camm made a wise decision, for it was the well-tried structure of the 'Hurricane', particularly that of the fuselage, which made it such a robust and easy to repair aircraft. Those features, coupled with the decision to produce them before the receipt of the official order, ensured that nearly 2,000 'Hurricanes' had been delivered by the beginning of the Battle of Britain of which some 400-500 had been lost, many on the ground in France, in the opening stages of the war. In fact, Fighter Command's strength for the Battle of Britain comprised more 'Hurricane' squadrons than those with 'Spitfires'.

But, back to the Hawker production of the 'Hurricane'. With the decision to go for an initial batch of 1,000 aircraft, a new factory would have to be provided in order to ensure that deliveries could be set at a high rate. For in 1936 Winston Churchill was asking questions in Parliament about the level of German rearmament funding, which had been estimated at £1 billion per annum, a huge sum for those days. Shortly after this Churchill managed to arrange a Privy Council meeting with Baldwin, the Prime Minister, at which he included this quote from his summary of that meeting:

> We must accelerate and simplify our aeroplane production and push it to the largest scale, and not hesitate to make contacts with the United States and elsewhere for the largest possible quantities of aviation material and equipment of all kinds. We are in danger, as we never have been in danger before.

Hawker's Board was obviously of the same mind and, now that the company was financially secure, were able to play their part in the strenuous preparations for fighter production, despite the Government's lack of impetus in dealing with the impending threat from Hitler and his minions, shortly to be countered by the Air Ministry's shadow factory scheme.

In the middle of all this political and industrial turmoil Sydney Camm and his team continued their 'Hurricane' refinements and production plans. In 1936, an initial £30,000 was made available for the construction of an additional factory and airfield at Parlaunt Park Farm, Langley in Buckinghamshire. It would be from this plant that the majority of Hawker's Hurricane production would be concentrated. The new factory was initially of 600,000 sq. ft area and cost £775,000. It was ready for occupation in June 1939. Whilst it was under construction 'Hurricane' final assembly was carried out at Brooklands, the first 500 or so aircraft having the fabric-covered wings which were subsequently replaced with new stressed skin metal ones before hostilities commenced seriously. The first production aircraft flew at Brooklands on 12th October, 1937, and by 31st October, 1939, 545 had been delivered from here. By the time production was phased out of Brooklands in 1941, a total of 2,815 Hurricanes had been built there.

The initial service experience with the 'Hurricane' was not without its problems. First to come to the design team's attention was that the three aircraft which had been dived through low cloud and had crashed, two on land and one into the sea. This was passed on to the flight test department which discovered that a large error in the altimeter reading, in the region of 2,000 ft, could occur in a high speed dive. This was due to the fact that the air pressure in the closed cockpit, an essential function to enable the altimeter to give a correct reading, was not changing at the same rate as that in the atmosphere outside. This gave the pilot a totally false impression of his height, particularly above the clouds where he had no ground reference. A modification to the source of this pressure from inside the cockpit to one taken from the outside static pressure fed to the airspeed indicator soon cured this. With the 'Hurricane' being the first closed cockpit fighter to be built by Hawker's, this vital change had not been realised as being essential. One question which has been unanswered in respect of this problem is, why had not flight testing shown it up?

With the great success of the 'Hart' and all its derivatives, Camm knew that with careful design, using major components and assemblies of the 'Hurricane' he could carry out a similar exercise. He had Ministry specification P.4/34 in mind initially. This was for a light tactical support bomber, the required maximum speed being 300 mph. With the 'Hurricane' employing detachable outer wings these could be used, minus their guns, on other aircraft, as could the tailplane and forward fuselage. The engine would of course be the 'Merlin'. Design started on what became the 'Henley' as soon as the 'Hurricane' detail design had been more or less completed. Construction of a prototype began in mid-1935, but was a slow process as the 'Hurricane' by now was top priority. The prototype did not fly from Brooklands until March 1937. After service trials an initial order for 350 was placed, and production commenced at the Gloster plant, but shortly after this the Air Ministry decided on a change of role, to that of target towing, and this order was reduced to 200. In its original offensive role the 'Henley' was a pleasant, viceless, aircraft to fly. However, in the target towing role problems appeared when the drag of some of the targets called for high engine powers at the slow speeds realised. This in its turn caused overheating problems and engine failures abounded. It had but a short service life and the survivors of a frightening attrition rate were to all intents and purposes withdrawn by the end of 1942. Camm's comments on this are not on record, but would have been quite outspoken, particularly as the demise of the 'Henley' was directly attributable to the fact that it was switched to a role for which it had not been designed.

A second design using 'Hurricane' components was the 'Hotspur'. This was designed to specification F.9/35 which called for a 'Demon' replacement employing an aft-mounted power-operated gun turret. It was not until 1938 that a prototype was available and Hawker's by then were so committed to the 'Hurricane' that no further work was done, with the single example finishing its days at Farnborough as a test aircraft on flap and dive brake trials. It had exhibited a maximum speed of 316 mph, some 20 mph greater than the Boulton & Paul 'Defiant', the only turret fighter to go into service with the RAF, which after an initial very brief success, largely because the Luftwaffe fighters did not expect opposing fire from behind the 'Defiant', was relegated to night fighter use.

However, back to the 'Hurricane' prototype. In February 1936, this had been delivered to the Aeroplane and Armament Experimental Establishment (A&AEE) at Martlesham Heath for the initial service evaluation trials. These trials proved to take longer than anticipated as, after the initial assessment

The Hawker 'Hotspur' turret fighter. The slower and heavier Boulton & Paul 'Defiant' was chosen in preference to this by the Ministry.   *BAE Systems*

which showed that the A&AEE were more than satisfied with the performance and handling of the aircraft, problems with the 'Merlin' engine appeared. The 'Merlin I', being liquid-cooled (Glycol, which was capable of very high temperature operation), was running at much higher temperatures than the previous water-cooled 'Kestrels'. This led to cylinder head cracking and consequent loss of cooling fluid. Rolls-Royce decided that an intensive ground and flight development programme was needed to test a redesigned cylinder head. A few 'Merlin I' engines were made available for the limited test flying possible whilst Rolls-Royce got down to the job of producing a fully tested 'Merlin II', but it was not until the autumn of 1937 that this new engine was available for production aircraft.

With the majority of the teething problems solved and the 'Hurricane' entering quantity production, the main task was to ensure that the aircraft were coming out in sufficient numbers as the threat of war grew ever closer.

As the 'Hurricane' production line got under way and aircraft were being delivered to the RAF, Camm was elected as a Member of Council of the Royal Aeronautical Society. This honour was accepted by him and many a council meeting must have been enlivened by his forthright remarks on some subjects being discussed.

As a guide to the acceleration in production of the 'Hurricane' and 'Spitfire' aircarft that took place around this time, in September 1938, the RAF had just 93 of these eight-gun fighters, including reserves, available. All were 'Hurricanes'. One year later, the total of immediately available fighters was in excess of 500 and by now the 'Spitfires', of which there were 187, had started to arrive.

By September 1939, as war commenced, the flow of 'Hurricane' production was steadily increasing and production was now under way at Kingston, Brooklands, Langley and Glosters at Hucclecote. Production rates were approximately three per day from the three Hawker sites and three per day from Glosters large plant. However, losses and the increasing number of damaged machines threatened to overtake production, so one extra responsibility which came Camm's way in these early days of the war was that of repairing the damaged 'Hurricanes'. Far too many of them were grounded for lack of spares or space in repair facilities. In June 1940 the number of unserviceable aircraft was growing at an alarming rate. The Brooklands and Langley sites were rearranged and had extra shops built to provide extra space for repair work by Hawker's. To cover the work on the technical side Camm drew some key people out of his team to cover the necessary work, delegating much of the responsibility to H.E.J. Rochefort from his stress group, who went on regular tours of the facilities holding the damaged aircraft in his Ford 8 saloon to assess the battle damage and decide on the appropriate repair schemes. This repair aid created by Hawker's, almost overnight, ensured that in 1940 alone, some 973 damaged 'Hurricanes' were repaired and returned to the squadrons. This was the beginning of a continued and expanded repair scheme, eventually to cover all production aircraft of all types which continued throughout the war.

Adequate replacements to fill the gaps caused by losses in France whilst supporting the British ground forces were now available, with a surplus to enable the home defence squadrons to be built up for the anticipated German onslaught on the United Kingdom. But it had been a close run thing, for at one period in France 'Hurricane' losses were 12 per day.

By the time the Battle of Britain began, 'Hurricanes' formed nearly 65 per cent of Fighter Command's strength, and deliveries of production aircraft were at 120 per month. By August some 200 aircraft a month were being delivered. The resulting slaughter of the Luftwaffe by 'Hurricanes' and 'Spitfires' halted the German plans for invasion and the UK was spared to go on and eventually turn the tide of the war in Europe.

By 1941 the 'Hurricane II' had been developed and was in production, to replace the early Mark I. Now the earlier aircraft had been upgraded with new propellers and the wings were the all-metal design. As much had been learnt from the operational use in the Battle of Britain, further improvements had been instigated to extend the life of a tough and reliable fighter. The previous year had seen the introduction of the four-digit Hawker project number, beginning with P.1001. P.1002 was the 'Hurricane II'. Three main versions of the 'Hurricane II' were to appear, the 'MkIIA', which was the standard eight-gun version with the 1,280 bhp 'Merlin XX', which raised the level speed to 342 mph from the 324 mph of the latest 'MkI'. Next came the 'MkIIB' with 12 machine guns in the wings, then the 'MkIIC' with four 20 mm Hispano cannon replacing the machine guns and finally, the specialized 'MkIID' with two 40 mm under-wing Vickers guns. This latter was specifically for attacks on armoured vehicles. Following these derivatives came a further modification whereby two 250 lb. bombs could be carried under the wings, and later this was increased to two 500 lb. bombs. The 'Hurricane' in its new fighter-bomber role proved so effective, particularly in the Middle and Far Eastern theatres, that production was extended past the end of the November 1941 cut-off planned to August 1944 as the new uses proliferated.

A 'Hurricane' Mk IIb of the Russian Air Force, one of over 3,000 supplied in 1942-1943.
BAE Systems

'Hurricane' Mk IIc supplied to the Turkish Air Force from stocks held for the North African campaign.   *BAE Systems*

LF363, a preserved Mk IIc 'Hurricane', attached to the Battle of Britain memorial flight, caught here at Dunsfold in about 1960.   *BAE Systems*

This Mk IId 'Hurricane' was a memorial aircraft for Squadron Leader John Gillan (presented by his mother).   *BAE Systems*

Mk II 'Hurricane' with two long range fuel tanks to enhance endurance.   *BAE Systems*

A 'Hurricane' of the Royal Canadian Air Force.   *BAE Systems*

The 'Hurricane' was a very strong aircraft indeed. There was no record of any one of them suffering structural failure when airborne. Out of a total of 14,500 built this fact alone signifies the sturdiness of the design. That was why the modifications to turn it into an effective fighter-bomber could be carried out without too much need to redesign major components greatly to accept the increased loadings that role implied.

The Langley production rate for the 'Hurricane' rose to 10 aircraft a day seven days a week at its peak. Also a completely duplicated line at the Gloster plant was set up and built some 2,750 of all marks until superseded by the 'Typhoon' production.

One major overseas production line was set up in Canada at the Canadian Car & Foundry Corporation in Montreal. This concern started setting up for production in the spring of 1938, the necessary drawings of tooling and parts being supplied, plus one aircraft off the Hawker production line to use as a guide. Considering that they managed to get matters running without the need for a dedicated team from Hawker's to come over to Canada to advise, this was a thoroughly capable operation, and emphasises the basic simplicity of the construction techniques so carefully developed by Camm over the years. A total of 1,451 Canadian 'Hurricanes' were delivered from March 1940, many direct to Russia after the entry of that country to the war on the Allies' side in 1941. The fate of the aircraft supplied to assist the Canadian organization in their production tasks is interesting. It was eventually returned to the UK in early 1942 and used for the trials of the Hillson slip-wing. This was a jettisonable top wing of identical planform to the standard 'Hurricane' wing which was intended to provide extra lift for take-off and initial climb. The idea for this emanated from the firm of Hill & Sons Ltd who made the necessary modifications and fitted an example for trials. A few flights were made under an Air Ministry contract before this scheme was finally abandoned. Probably the thoughts of a batch of wings fluttering to the ground in the vicinity of an airfield put this feasible but impracticable scheme to bed.

Another modification unique to the Canadian-produced 'Hurricanes' was the fitting of a ski undercarriage to one of the 'MkXII' variants (the standard production type for the Canadian operation). This was a fixed unit and must have affected the level speed performance somewhat, and little is known about any further variants being converted. Like the slip-wing exercise it faded into obscurity.

When the threat of German air raids on Langley was at its height, a 'Hurricane' was set aside and kept there. Fully-armed, it was on readiness every day to counter any attack, if sufficient advance warning were given. However, after a few abortive raids during which bombs were dropped near the factory, Langley was left alone and production was unaffected.

The robustness of the 'Hurricane' airframe had enabled it to be adapted to many roles. From the basic interceptor design it had graduated to ground attack with cannon, bombs and rocket projectiles, naval fighter capable of carrier operation and the unique 'Hurricat' or catapult-launched 'Hurricane' carried by some merchant 'CAM' ships in convoy. These unique aircraft succeeded in shooting down several German four-engined 'Condor' long range reconnaissance aircraft shadowing convoys, but had the disadvantage of

The Hillson slip-wing 'Hurricane'. The top wing was used for take-off and climb before being jettisoned. Just how any other aircraft in the vicinity were to avoid the falling wing is not known. Needless to say the idea never took off!

BAE Systems

A 'Hurricane' Mk IV, with two 40 mm Vickers cannon.   *BAE Systems*

A 'Hurricane' Mk IV, with two 40mm Vickers cannon at Langley in 1942-1943. At this time the production rate for all marks was eight aircraft per day at this site.   *BAE Systems*

The last 'Hurricane' built of some 14,500 examples, 'The Last of the Many'. This is now preserved in the Battle of Britain memorial flight.   *BAE Systems*

having to ditch after the action, due to having insufficient fuel to make it to a home base from far out in the Atlantic. This sometimes involved the loss of the pilot.

In later years, even some special two-seat trainers appeared for a few foreign customers. Camm's design, with suitable modifications for extreme climates, proved its worth in all theatres of the war in these roles.

Before closing the 'Hurricane' story, there is one gem of an account of the prototype which, it is thought was the only such aircraft to achieve a kill in the war. One of the wartime test pilots was flying the still fully operational and updated prototype, which was in use as a communications machine by Hawker's, and had been fitted with a full complement of eight guns, which happened on this occasion to be armed. Somewhere over Surrey he came upon a lone Dornier 'Do17' and promptly shot it down. Clearly in those early days of the war aircraft, including some on test or communications, whenever possible, flew with the guns armed, 'just in case'. The prototype was said to have been airworthy up to 1942, but no records seem to exist concerning its subsequent fate.

It was in 1941 that Camm was invited to become a member of the Advisory Committee of the Royal Aeronautical Society which was set up to provide advice to the Ministry of Aircraft Production. He took advantage of this membership to put forward his views on the need for development, quality and research to meet the post-war needs of the aircraft industry. Despite some crucial advice from this august body being totally ignored, Camm and the other members saw to it that, where necessary, repeated submissions were made in an effort to hammer home their views.

This year also brought him the award of the CBE in recognition of his work in leading the design of the 'Hurricane' and its successors thus far.

The two-seat 'Hurricane' trainer provided to the Persian Air Force in 1945. *BAE Systems*

The 'Tornado' prototype, predecessor to the BAE Systems 'Typhoon'.

Chapter Six

More Fighters

It may not be generally realized, but the specification for the Hawker 'Tornado', F.18/37, seems to have been influenced by Camm's proposals of 1936 for a 400 mph interceptor to supersede the 'Hurricane'. If not, certainly it paralleled Camm's thoughts. His forward thinking was certainly that of vastly increased speeds being necessary for future fighters.

Camm, once the 'Hurricane' was firmly in production and rolling out at a respectable rate, began thinking about the successor. Taking the current F.18/37 specification prepared for a single-seat interceptor he had two versions of the same design drawn up which were offered to meet this requirement. The first was powered by a Rolls-Royce 'Vulture' of 1,760 bhp and the second by the Napier 'Sabre' of 2,180 bhp. Despite the Ministry's concern about the use of such large engines in a single-seat fighter, Camm knew this was the only way to go if the 400 mph speed was to be achieved. This was particularly so as the wing was still of a thick section.

The 'Sabre' engine was somewhat delayed due to problems in its development in the early days so the aircraft, known as the 'Tornado', started life with the Rolls-Royce 'Vulture'. Kingston received the 'Vulture' for the prototype from Rolls-Royce in December 1938 when the new fighter was under construction. It was not until July 1939 that it would be moved to Langley, from where the first flight was made on 6th October. The performance showed promise from the start, with a maximum speed of over 380 mph. Further flight trials confirmed this speed and soon an order for 500 'Tornados' was placed by the Air Ministry.

Following this promising start, trouble appeared with the Rolls-Royce 'Vulture', which began to show problems with connecting rod failures. Also pressure of other work in the aircraft industry delayed the plans to produce the 'Tornados' in quantity. But by the summer of 1941 the production site had been implemented at A.V. Roe & Co. who were already building and delivering the 'Manchester' bomber using the 'Vulture' engines. However, the 'Vulture' failure rate was unacceptable, resulting in the loss of several 'Manchesters' and Rolls-Royce decided to discontinue the production and supply of the troublesome engine in order to concentrate more on the 'Merlin'. One production 'Tornado' had been turned out and delivered to Langley where it was eventually passed on to propeller manufacturers Rotols at Staverton and de Havilland Propellers at Hatfield for use as a propeller flying test-bed.

By early 1940, as the British and French forces in Europe were being pushed back to the Channel coast and the threat of German bombing of England grew, it was decided to move the Hawker Design Office out of its Kingston site. The new location was in nearby Esher at Claremont House where Camm relocated with his teams. This move proved a wise one for later that year an air raid by the Luftwaffe resulted in the Production Process Department building in Kingston, just across the road from that previously holding the Design Offices, receiving a direct hit and it was virtually destroyed. Luckily, the night shift,

R7881, a 'Typhoon' of the first production batch built at Gloster Aircraft.   *BAE Systems*

'Typhoon' FB Mk Ib with typical ground attack load of rocket projectiles and four cannon.
BAE Systems

then on duty, had repaired to the shelters and escaped injury. However, a night-watchman had, for some reason, stayed at his post, and was killed. With the move to Claremont and the more spacious accommodation this offered Camm took the advantage of reorganizing the Design Office into a new structure with one group being a Project Office. The remainder stayed as they were. The new set-up was expressly for aerodynamic studies and performance prediction which, he realized, were to become key disciplines. He was not going to be caught out as the art of aircraft design advanced.

One day in 1940, at the height of the Battle of Britain, a German fighter swept low over Thames Ditton and the pilot decided to take a few pot shots at the houses there. Some of his wild shots spread across the Camm garden and splinters flew from the woodwork of the house. Hilda Camm was in the house and the sudden shock of the bombardment caused her to drop the tray she was carrying. She turned to her husband nearby and said: 'Syd! I'm not staying in this house one more night!' The net result was that the whole family moved out to the Claremont offices and slept in the cellars on camp-beds, until matters had quietened down somewhat.

In keeping with his World War I trips to inspect captured enemy aircraft, during World War II Camm also went to Farnborough to look over the 'Me109' and 'Fw190' after their capture, inspecting them thoroughly. These German aircraft were, after all, the opponents of his own fighter designs and he wished to see if any design features they embodied might be of use to himself in the future.

Around the time when the move to Claremont had taken place, Camm had noted the problems with the 'Vulture' and had made the suggestion that the new Bristol 'Centaurus' 18-cylinder 2,210 bhp air-cooled radial engine should be suitable as an alternative power-plant. A second prototype appeared shortly after the first with the 'Centaurus' fitted and, after initial flight trials gave a top speed of 402 mph; the cancelling of the 'Vulture'-engined 'Tornado' saw this promising alternative-engined fighter remain a prototype. The work done thus far was not wasted as later on there came a series of radial-engined fighters which saw Hawker's as major producers of such types up to the jet age.

The 'Tornado' thus died and much of the work done on the Napier 'Sabre' version now took precedence. This variant became the 'Typhoon', which first flew in February 1940. Testing continued through to September 1941, when the first production machines were delivered to the RAF from the Gloster factory which was to build all the 'Typhoons'. By the end of that year 150 had been delivered and problems had arisen, the worst being the loss of several aircraft due to the failure of the rear fuselage, which broke off in flight, generally at a high speed. It was not until a 'Typhoon' suffered such a loss on a test flight, killing the test pilot, Kenneth Seth-Smith, that it was discovered that the elevator balance weight bracket had fractured due to fatigue. This led to a catastrophic imbalance of the elevator which caused the surface to flutter violently. The loads imposed on the rear fuselage were such that it failed and broke off. The bracket was strengthened and the trouble disappeared. The 'Typhoon' thus acquired a bad name early in its life which nearly caused its withdrawal from service altogether.

One other unfortunate fact about the new fighter was its similarity, at a distance, to the new German Focke-Wulf 'Fw190' fighter. Several 'Typhoons' were bounced and one or two shot down by 'Spitfires' because of this. Its

'Typhoon' JN729.   *BAE Systems*

A 'Typhoon', DN411, of the third production batch, a Gloster machine.   *BAE Systems*

manoeuvrability was not equal to either the 'Fw190' or the 'Spitfire' and clearly its days as an interceptor were numbered.

However, the low-level performance was exceptional so after trials with various weapon loads, the 'Typhoons' were switched from their interception role to that of ground attack which, up to 1943, had been largely covered by the 'Hurricane' fighter-bombers. These could not cope with the 'Fw190' fighter opposition due to the speed advantage of the German fighter, but the 'Typhoon' could at low level. The most effective weapon for ground attack was found to be the 3 inch rocket projectile, of which eight could be carried. The rockets, backed up by the fire from the four 20 mm cannon were a lethal combination in operations against shipping, land transport or even military installations. The fire power of one 'Typhoon' was equivalent to that of an average Royal Navy destroyer with this weapon fit.

Altogether, some 3,330 'Typhoons' were built, all by Glosters, before being overtaken by Camm's next creation, the 'Tempest'. Originally known as the 'Typhoon II', it was renamed 'Tempest' in early 1942. The Air Ministry had issued specification F.10/41, for yet another interceptor fighter which Camm discussed with the Director of Technical Development at the Ministry. Out of the discussion came the idea that with a new thinner wing on the 'Typhoon', a new version of the Napier 'Sabre' combined with wing leading edge radiators might give considerably improved performance all round. The resulting design analysis carried out by his Project Office promised speeds well in excess of 400 mph. The 'Tempest' was, in fact, to become one of the most effective Allied fighters in the latter years of the war.

It was the complete redesign of the wing which made the 'Tempest' the outstanding fighter that it was. The 'Hurricane' and 'Typhoon' had thick wings, primarily because Camm seemed unable to accept that thinner sections could be just as strong when properly designed. At the maximum speeds applicable to these earlier aircraft the thick wings were satisfactory, but with a new design theoretically capable of speeds well over 400 mph in level flight, the diving speeds were going to be 500 mph-plus. Thick wings displayed uncomfortable effects such as buffeting and aileron control problems at high speeds, and these would result in the pilot not being able to use his gun sights satisfactorily and the weapon aiming would be inaccurate.

Camm had recognized these facts after de-briefing of the test pilots following some high speed testing of the 'Typhoon' and so it was natural to consider how to alleviate the situation. The thinner wing was the obvious answer, particularly to improve the buffeting. So the new Project Office was set the task of deciding what the new wing should be like. The resulting design, the 'Tempest', was an excellent one and the general concept was to be carried over to the end of piston-engined fighter design at Hawker's.

Once the Project Office had completed its task on this new development, the design was tendered to the Ministry specification F.10/41 and such was the confidence in Camm and his team that a contract for 400 aircraft was placed in August 1942 before the first flight of one of the six prototypes on the 2nd September. The 'Mark I' prototype, due to problems with the Napier 'Sabre IV' engine destined for it, did not fly until February 1943, but immediately showed an outstanding level speed of 466 mph at 24,500 ft altitude. It never got to the

A 'Tempest' Mk II, with the Bristol 'Centaurus' radial engine.   *BAE Systems*

'Tempest II' PR533 was used at Langley and the A&AEE for flight trials.   *Unknown source*

production stage as Napiers had problems with the 'Sabre IV' and withdrew it from production. It was the only 'Tempest' to have the wing leading edge radiator system which clearly gave it this exceptional speed. The rest of the liquid-cooled versions all would have the familiar chin radiator cooling system.

With the 'Tempest', the old Hawker steel tube fuselage structure had been kept in the forward portion with the complete rear fuselage structure being a monocoque stressed-skin one. Whilst the old steel tube arrangement was still structurally sound it was outdated, as the monocoque structure gave more internal space and made it easier to fit internal features and equipment.

There were to be six marks of the 'Tempest' altogether, of which three were ordered into production, the first being the 'Mark II' which was powered by the Bristol 'Centaurus' 2,520 hp air-cooled radial engine. This was the fastest of the breed at 442 mph. The second the 'Mark V' with the Napier 'Sabre II' of 2,180hp which could manage 426 mph and lastly the 'Mark VI' with the 2,340hp Napier 'Sabre V' which was capable of 438 mph.

The excellent level speed performance of the 'Tempest' made it a natural for countering the German 'V1' flying bomb menace. With special high octane fuel for the engines to enhance the low level speed they could overhaul the 'V1s' to shoot them down. A hazardous task as they often had no chance of avoiding the result of the explosion of the 'V1'. Another, very effective and safer way was to fly alongside the bomb and tip its wing with that of the 'Tempest' to send the weapon spiralling out of control into the ground. One of the first 'V1s' to be shot down by the RAF fell to a 'Tempest' on 16th June, 1944. Out of a total of 1,771 'V1s' shot down by fighters 638 fell to 'Tempests', this score being amassed between 13th June and 5th September. A great effort was put into countering the 'V1s' by the RAF which even pressed the brand new Gloster 'Meteor' jet into service, however the souped-up 'Tempest' was the faster at that stage.

Later, in the final six months of the war, 'Tempests' sometimes came up against the new Messerschmitt 'Me262' jet fighter, shooting down 11 of these potent and agile machines. No other Allied fighter was to reach this score.

It was only the 'Tempest V' which saw extensive service with the RAF. The 'Marks II and VI' were delayed into production at Glosters due to the priority being given to the Gloster 'Meteor' jet fighter and so production was temporarily transferred to the Bristol Aircraft Company's plant at Weston-super-Mare before a further transfer to Langley. The whole of the 'Mark V' production came from Langley which had plenty of capacity after the cessation of 'Hurricane' production in 1944. In all a total of 1,394 production versions were built. Some of those completed after the end of the war were eventually transferred to India (89) and Pakistan (24) from RAF stocks as those countries built up their armed forces after the splitting of the old India into the two countries. A total of 528 orders for 'Tempests' was cancelled after the war, 30 of this number from Bristols, as the country started to get back to normal peace-time life.

By far the best performer was the 'Centaurus'-powered 'Mark II', and this was to form the basis for the final Hawker piston-engined fighter family, the 'Fury'.

In 1943, specification F.6/42 came to the notice of Camm, who was already thinking in terms of a smaller lighter variant of the 'Tempest' with a Bristol 'Centaurus' radial engine which, being air-cooled, eliminated the need for a

A 'Tempest' Mk V, HM595, at Langley.   *BAE Systems*

'Tempest' Mk V NV768 used for trials of the Napier ducted spinner which was fitted in conjuction with an annular radiator.   *BAE Systems*

complex liquid cooling system thus helping the light weight aimed for. The draft schemes for his approach to this proposal were submitted, following which the Ministry re-wrote F.6/42 to produce F.2/43. In April 1943 yet another specification N.7/43 for a naval interceptor fighter appeared. After studying this Camm suggested to the Ministry of Aircraft Production (MAP) that the F.2/43 could also meet N.7/43 if an uprated 'Centaurus' was employed. The MAP immediately saw the logic in this and the RAF and Naval requirements were pooled under F.2/43. Hawker's split the workload of design and development, covering the land-based version themselves and contracting out the naval version to Boulton & Paul Aircraft Ltd at Wolverhampton.

It was the Hawker prototype that took to the air first in September 1944 and, during the extensive flight test programme, when fitted with a trial installation of the Napier 'Sabre VII' engine, attained a maximum level speed of 485 mph. This was the fastest of any Hawker piston-engined fighter. Camm was quietly proud of this achievement as it was not far short of that currently attained by the early jets, the Gloster 'Meteor' and de Havilland 'Vampire'. However, the war was clearly coming to a close and his expertise, although still needed, was not so much in demand, but current developments were to radically change the fighter scene. The advent of the jet engine presented a new challenge and promised a big change in design philosophy. Hawker's was a military aircraft producer and some interim type was needed to cover the gap between the cessation of wartime production and the inevitable new breed of high performance gas turbine-powered fighters.

In 1945 Camm's mother still lived in the family house in Alma Road, Windsor and was present at the VE day street party held to commemorate the end of the war in Europe. By this time Camm's name was much mentioned in connection with his 'Hurricane' fighter which many realized had done so much for the country in a long and difficult war.

It was the naval version of the 'Fury', the 'Sea Fury', which kept matters going with Hawker's in the years after the war. It had entered production as the war ended, with 50 interceptors and 50 fighter-bombers being ordered in late 1944. Capable of 460 mph in level flight, the fighter version upgraded the Fleet Air Arm's capability considerably and, after deck landing trials on HMS *Victorious*, entered service. The aircraft carrier had proved itself a very effective way of positioning air power and the Royal Navy in those days had a good number in service deployed around the world. With the current aircraft in service somewhat dated and war-weary it was sensible to re-equip the Fleet Air Arm with new interceptors and fighter-bombers, so the 'Sea Fury' was an ideal answer to its needs. Production ran through to 1951, with a total of 666 being ordered of the single-seater type, plus 60 of the two-seat trainer variant. A considerable number of export orders were also received from Holland, Iraq, Pakistan, Egypt and Burma, totalling 190 aircraft which kept the production line busy until the 'Sea Hawk' and 'Hunter' appeared and swept away the piston-engined family once and for all.

The 'Sea Fury' was the last of the line of piston-engined fighters to see active service with the Fleet Air Arm, this being in the Korean War from 1950 as a fighter-bomber. In this conflict some even took on the Russian-built 'MiG15' jets, actually managing to down at least one, but not without loss to themselves.

The second prototype 'Fury' monoplane fighter, with the Bristol 'Centaurus' engine and five-bladed propeller at Langley in 1945. This type was to be developed into the 'Sea Fury'.

BAE Systems

A 'Sea Fury' with wings folded.   *Unknown source*

A 'Sea Fury' about to pick up a wire during a carrier deck landing.   *BAE Systems*

A 'Sea Fury' overflies a battleship of the fleet.   *BAE Systems*

An air to air photograph of the 'P.1040'.   *BAE Systems*

Chapter Seven

Into the Jet Age: I

As the war progressed, Camm became aware of the jet engine being developed by Power Jets Ltd under Frank Whittle, which by 1941 was in the stage of being prepared in the form of the Whittle 'W.1' for initial test flights in the Gloster 'E.28/39' experimental aircraft. He naturally took an interest in this and the Project Office began to gather what little information was available on this new top secret revolutionary engine. Gloster's by this time had received a specification F.9/40 from the Ministry for consideration on the design of a twin-engined jet-powered interceptor, to become the 'Meteor', and the project design team at Hucclecote were starting some schemes to try and satisfy the requirements. The 'Meteor' was to be somewhat delayed into service due to protracted development problems with the engines and the first deliveries were therefore not made until May 1944, just before the onset of the invasion of France.

With the jet engine as a reality from 1941, as the Project Office was engaged in studying a high-speed bomber, the 'P.1005', Camm began to think about using the jet to power this. The initial bomber design employed two Napier 'Sabre' engines, and some studies were made replacing the 'Sabres' with Power Jet engines. However, the current jet engine studies proved to be of too low a power and this project, given the designation 'P.1011', was terminated.

This abortive jet-powered project was followed by the 'P.1014', a single-seat fighter with a single Power Jet engine, but this too was shelved. However, the advent of the jet engine was kept alive by sundry studies as time permitted with the top priority being given to the range of piston-engined fighters still under development. Camm preferred to wait until the engine manufacturers had something better available. His philosophy was to let others iron out the problems before he, himself, was happy to take on a new concept of this nature. With hindsight, one can see the logic behind this reasoning, as it ensured that problems during the development of an aircraft employing something as revolutionary as the jet engine should be minimized. This particularly applied in times of war, where speed of production of the new designs was imperative.

Whilst continuing to develop his piston-engined family of fighters, Camm took note of the early jet-engined aircraft which had proved themselves in limited service as the war ended. He could see the potential offered by this new form of propulsion and the news that the Germans had also been engaged in producing jet fighters encouraged his resolve to get involved soon. He had, it is said, been asked to consider designing the first British jet aircraft, but that this offer was rejected. Whether this was due to his natural caution in stepping into the unknown, but this response was more likely to have been decided by the very heavy workload on him and his team in connection with the 'Hurricane' developments and the 'Typhoon' and 'Tempest' design programmes.

The Project Office did, however, start some schemes for a jet fighter in 1944 as a Private Venture exercise and from their initial thoughts emerged the 'P.1040'. The first drawing of this project appeared on 23rd December, 1944 as the Germans made their final push into the Ardennes. This scheme used the 'Tempest' outer wings and showed, for the first time, the distinctive split tail pipe exhausting aft of the mid wing trailing edge, a feature which was to stay for some time on the Hawker jets until the 'P.1081' and the 'Hunter' appeared. Accordingly, Camm saw to it that a tender was submitted in order to get a response in the form of a specification. This was a long time in coming as the ending of the war threw Ministry planning into turmoil. By October 1945 he was confident enough to recommend that the company proceed to manufacture a prototype with the issue of a production order.

At about this time the RAF interest lost momentum as the Ministry could not see much of an advance over the Gloster 'Meteor', which had just set a new world speed record of 606 mph. However, the Admiralty still retained a interest, seeing the 'P.1040' as a potential fleet support fighter. This spurred Camm to submit a further tender in January 1946, which resulted in specification N.7/46 being prepared and an instruction to proceed on three prototypes and one test specimen was issued, which was followed in May of that year by the contract.

With the war over and the country recovering to normality and with Camm increasingly busy with his jet fighter developments, matters at home took a new turn. Unknown to her parents his daughter, so often the subject of conversation in odd moments at the office, had entered a serious relationship with a young man. He lived in nearby Teddington and was a musician by profession. Phyllis married Lionel Dickson at Staines Registry Office on 18th July, 1947 and arrived home a few days later with a husband in tow. One wonders at Camm's first thoughts for a member of that profession as a son-in-law, but the fact that his father was a civil engineer might have helped along the way.

The 'P.1040' with Bill Humble in the cockpit.   *Unknown source*

Meantime the detail design and construction of the first example of the naval fighter proceeded and on 2nd September, 1947 the 'P.1040' flew at Boscombe Down. This prototype was devoid of armaments and folding wings required by the Navy, but was aerodynamically representative of the final production aircraft apart from minor changes to the outer wing taper. The power-plant was a Rolls-Royce 'Nene I' turbo-jet of 4,500 lb. thrust. One problem quickly showed itself, this being a tendency of the aircraft to 'wander' directionally. The prototype had large rectangular fairings aft of the jet pipes to protect the rear fuselage structure from excessive heating due to the jet exhaust blast. Corrections from the rudder only compounded the problem which was eventually solved by replacing the rectangular fairings with triangular, or pen-nib, fairings, whereupon the wandering ceased.

A year of test flying then took place whilst the design was navalised and the first such prototype was built. This flew on 3rd September, 1948 from Boscombe Down and was soon involved on the official assessment flying by the Ministry and service pilots, culminating in an initial series of deck take-off and landing trials on HMS *Illustrious* before being returned to Hawker's in July for new outer wings of slightly increased span. Following this modification it returned to the service testing and evaluation, during which it was flown at the 1949 Society of British Aircraft Constructors (SBAC) flying display. In November the 'Sea Hawk', as it had now been named, returned to the *Illustrious* for the final deck trials. Hawker's had, by this time, received a contract for 151 production aircraft.

With the undoubted success of his earlier piston-engined range of designs, as he entered the jet age with the 'Sea Hawk', Camm received the British Gold Medal of the Royal Aeronautical Society in 1949.

It was the 'Sea Hawk' and 'Sea Fury' orders up to the early 1950s which played a big part in keeping Hawker's in a healthy financial condition such that the company could continue its planning for future fighters. Camm also had high regard for the Royal Navy, as he himself was heard to say: 'They always treated us as though we were gentlemen'. He had come to grips with the jet era and was now intent on furthering the work in the Project Office which was being carried out in 1947. Designated 'P.1067', this was project proposed to employ the new axial-flow compressor Rolls-Royce 'A.J.65' turbo-jet which itself was a radical departure from the, by now, dated 'Nene' centrifugal compressor engines.

The 'P.1067', to become the classic 'Hunter', was spurred along by the onset of the Korean War, which brought home to the RAF and Fleet Air Arm the urgent need for more modern jet fighters and fighter-bombers to counter aircraft such as the Russian 'MiG15'. Accordingly, in addition to encouraging the research programme instigated by Camm at Hawker's based on variants of the 'P.1040', some hastily amended specifications were written by the Ministry calling for a wide range of aircraft types to replace those already in service.

The 'P.1040' had given Hawker's a sound basic jet-powered design and it was this that formed the basis for a comprehensive research programme into the quest for very high speeds which, it was recognized, needed to be achieved to counter adequately the opposing types in any future conflict.

The benefits of wing and tailplane sweep were by now confirmed as leading to the high speed performance needed and, as the design and manufacture of the prototype 'P.1067' was going to take some considerable time, Camm managed to arrange a

VP613, the first of the two 'Sea Hawk' prototypes.   *BAE Systems*

One of the two 'Sea Hawk' prototypes, VP422, ordered in 1947.   *BAE Systems*

'Sea Hawk' prototype with wings folded.   *BAE Systems*

'Sea Hawk' after a catapult launch from a carrier (see strap falling free).   *Unknown source*

A 'Sea Hawk' on home ground.

BAE Systems

series of discussions with the Air Ministry and Ministry of Supply, commencing in October 1946, for a research aircraft embodying a 35 degree swept wing. Specification E.38/46 was received in January 1947 and in March a tender was submitted. This was given the designation 'P.1052' and was in outline basically a 'Sea Hawk' with a swept wing. Shortly afterwards, a contract covering the production of two prototypes was received. This was to be the second British swept wing aircraft, the first being the DH108 of 1946. Considerable support for this proposal had come from the Royal Aircraft Establishment who were most interested in it providing vital information on the characteristics of swept wings to add to their design information.

As a matter of interest the interest in swept wings had started life as the 'P.1047', a rocket-powered interceptor, in which little interest could be generated. The 'P.1047' had appeared in 1945 as a project study, being basically the 'P.1040' with a 40 degree swept wing and represented one of the earliest, if not the earliest, swept wing designs in the UK. However, it never progressed beyond the drawing board. The advent of the swept wing for Hawker's was to come in 1948 with the 'P.1052' derivative of the 'P.1040'. Additionally, the 'P.1047' had been designed with a rocket motor in the rear fuselage to supplement the jet engine. The use of a rocket booster certainly gave excellent level speed performance at all altitudes and conferred a high rate of climb, but this device was later to be found somewhat risky following an in-flight explosion on the 'P.1072' research prototype embodying it, in addition to having the disadvantage of a limited time of operation due to the restricted fuel capacity. The pilot for the flight on which the explosion occurred was Neville Duke, who wrote: 'The thing exploded and set fire to the tail of the aircraft, so I shut down the rocket and landed'. Although those on the ground at Dunsfold were waiting for the aircraft to come to a fiery end, the structural integrity was such that it was possible for Duke to effect a safe landing and let the fire engines do their job. That, effectively, was the end of the rocket booster trials once and for all, for the reheat concept for jet engines had, by now, been proven and was a much more reliable means of achieving increased powers. Camm never did like the use of reheat and only the speed record 'Hunter' was to employ it. In fact no Hawker production aircraft, including those designed and built under the British Aerospace mantle, ever embodied it.

As the 'Sea Hawk' production was not to materialize until 1949, the advent of the 'P.1052' was essentially making that design obsolescent as it entered service. However, the research results gained led to the conversion of the second prototype 'P.1052' to a variant with a fully swept tail surfaces and a new rear fuselage which embodied a straight through single jet pipe in place of the split jet pipe of the 'P.1052'. This conversion was designated the 'P.1081'. The gradual approach to the all-swept configuration showed Camm's natural caution in going to such a layout, he wished to be absolutely sure that if there were any unknowns, the stage by stage approach would show them up. However, no alarming characteristics presented themselves.

The 'P.1081' confirmed in Camm's mind that future jet fighters were, in the main, to have fully swept flying surfaces and should, eventually, be capable of supersonic flight. Several flight tests into the high subsonic speed range were being carried out in this variant which, even with the low-powered Rolls-Royce 'Nene' engine, had reached Mach numbers in the region of 0.90, compared to the Mach 0.84 of the 'Sea Hawk' with the same power plant. There had been a possibility that the 'P.1081' could have been produced to answer a need for an operational version for the Australian Government, but this scheme never took off and it died in 1950.

The 'P.1052', the start of the transition to a swept surface aircraft.   *BAE Systems*

The 'P.1052' undergoing deck trials on HMS *Eagle*.   *BAE Systems*

'P.1072' rocket motor to augment the jet engine undergoes a test. *BAE Systems*

The fully swept 'P.1081': the aircraft that so nearly got to the production stage. Note the Supermarine 'Attacker' in the background, the only British jet to have a tail wheel undercarriage. *BAE Systems*

Dunsfold airfield and buildings shortly after the take-over by Hawker's in 1950. The aircraft in view comprise a pair of 'Hunters', plus two 'Sea Hawks' and the communications de Havilland 'Rapide'.

BAE Systems

Chapter Eight

Into the Jet Age: II

Meantime, the detail design of the 'P.1067' and the construction of the first of three prototypes had begun at Kingston whilst the research aircraft had been built and flown to provide information for confirmation of the concept.

The first 'P.1067' prototype was at an advanced stage of construction when tragedy struck. The 'P.1081', on 3rd April, 1951, had been on a test flight from Farnborough where it was then based. The pilot was Hawker's chief test pilot 'Wimpy' Wade. He had just returned from the United States where he had been sent to gain some experience on American jet aircraft, some of which were showing promise of good high speed potential.

The 'P.1081' crashed near Lewes. Wade had baled out, but it is thought that his ejection seat malfunctioned and he was killed. The exact cause of the accident was never discovered, although it has been speculated that Wade was in a high speed dive at the time and control had been lost due to unexpected effects at the extreme speed reached. This speculation is based on the fact that, according to some who were in the area of the crash, a sound like a sharp clap of thunder preceded the impact, so possibly Wade had gone supersonic in the dive and control had been compromised, or even lost, as a result. This has never been corroborated so, although a logical explanation, it must remain purely speculative.

Camm was devastated by the loss of Wade. He always regarded his test pilots as very special people and arranged for John Lidbury, the Company Secretary, and Neville Duke, one of the other test pilots who was a good friend of Wade's, to go and break the sad news to Wade's wife, Josephine. Wade was to be the last fatality amongst the Dunsfold test pilots until the mid-1980s, this being an outstanding record for a company involved in the high-speed combat aircraft sphere, particularly in those early days when the type of transonic flying being investigated was very much in its infancy.

Camm and his team were saddened by this loss to the company, but the work on the 'P.1067' continued and, on 20th July, 1951, the first prototype flew from Boscombe Down in the capable hands of the new chief test pilot, Neville Duke. A production contract for 113 aircraft had actually preceded this first flight by some four months. This indicates the continued confidence placed by the Ministry in Camm and his jet developments. This first flight took place after some considerable taxi trials, which culminated in a high speed run along Boscombe Down's long runway during which Duke eased back the control column to achieve a short hop. The amount of runway remaining was barely sufficient to put down and brake to a sufficiently slow speed to turn off at the end. In fact the brakes burnt out in the process and, as Duke laconically put it: 'We made a note that the time seems to be past when you can do hops with high powered prototypes unless you have tremendously long runways'.

Coinciding with the first flight of what was to become a classic aircraft, Camm was elected to the Chairmanship of the Technical Board of the Society of

Another aerial view of Dunsfold airfield and buildings in 1950.

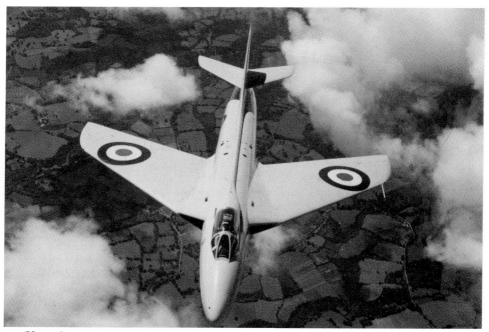

'Hunter' prototype. *BAE Systems*

The prototype 'Hunter', with chief test pilot Neville Duke standing in the cockpit.

BAE Systems

'Hunter' prototype.   *BAE Systems*

WB188, the prototype 'Hunter' converted to Mk III standard. The only 'Hunter' to be fitted with re-heat. This aircraft was used on the successful attempt on the world absolute speed record in 1953. The aircraft has been preserved and can be found at the Tangmere Museum near Chichester.   *BAE Systems*

British Aircraft Constructors. He was to hold this prestigious position until 1953.

Throughout all the design and project work associated with the experimental aircraft based on the 'Sea Hawk', Camm had maintained a close association with the RAE Aerodynamics Department, particularly as the 'P.1067' was being schemed. The advice from this key research centre was to keep the layout as slim and streamlined as possible. This applied to the flying surfaces in particular, his earlier insistence on the thicker wings as used on the piston-engined fighters was curtailed in the interests of obtaining a good high speed performance. Likewise the fuselage was recommended to be no more than 50 inches maximum diameter. As the intended engine was some 40 inches overall in diameter, fitting it into the fuselage was going to be a tricky job.

As all the development aircraft gathered information and the 'P.1067' prototypes took shape Hawker's were in the process of reorganizing their sites. The Canbury Park Road production facilities were to be gradually phased out, now that the 20-year lease of the Richmond Road factory originally used by Sopwith's during World War I, set up with the Leyland Motor Company in 1928, had come to an end. Also the assembly plant and airfield at Langley was not ideally sited now, as it was only six miles from the rapidly growing new London airport at Heathrow. Additionally, the Langley field had no hard runways and was not at all suitable for the new generation of jets. This closure of Langley was primarily why the 'Sea Hawk' production was contracted out to the Armstrong Whitworth plant at Baginton, Coventry, the airfield there having hard runways, as the imminent tooling up for the 'P.1067' would absorb all of Hawker's production space elsewhere. Only 35 'Sea Hawks' ever emerged from Kingston out of the total of 554 built. Then, in 1948, the company acquired the tenancy of the old wartime airfield at Dunsfold in Surrey. This had a good long concrete runway and was in a part of Surrey free of any industrial haze and commercial air traffic, and so was ideal. In later years it was to find itself on the approach/departure path for Gatwick and was to be designated as an emergency alternate airfield for that airport should times of emergency call for any diversions. The Langley site was gradually phased out and closed as the last reconditioned 'Sea Furys' were dealt with in 1958, after which the site was vacated.

The importance of the 'Hunter' as a modern fighter was realized at an early stage, not only by the RAF, but by Hawker's as well. One important design feature was the removable gun pack, containing the four Aden cannon plus the associated ammunition storage. This enabled an empty weapons fit to be speedily changed for a new loaded pack in the minimum of time. The 'Hunter' was to run to 10 versions for the RAF, with production spread over eight years. Also four of the 10 versions were to bring in several sizeable export orders to Holland, Sweden, Switzerland and India and two versions were licence-built in Holland and Belgium. In later years, as those in the RAF were replaced by the supersonic 'Lightning', many were bought back by Hawker's and refurbished for other export sales to Denmark, India, Iraq, Jordan, Kuwait, Chile, Qatar, Lebanon, Rhodesia, Peru, Saudi Arabia, Singapore, Abu Dhabi and Kenya. It was truly an international fighter. The importance of the 'Hunter' laying a foundation for future sales to the Gulf States cannot be emphasized too much.

The first production 'Hunter' WT555 was used for the handling trials prior to the service entry
for the type.   *BAE Systems*

A production 'Hunter' WT594 of the first production batch.   *BAE Systems*

From the experiences of the air forces of the countries involved with the 'Hunter' has come a steady flow of orders for British fighter and combat aircraft to that part of the world which still goes on today. The excellence of Camm's design saw to the establishment of that. It was this classic design that confirmed Hawker's were still at the top of the league for the supply of such aircraft to many air forces all over the world until the sheer might and financial clout of the United States aerospace industry saw to the ascendancy of that country's aircraft on a world-wide basis. Hawker's eventually suffered by not having a supersonic successor to the 'Hunter' accepted at a time when the disastrous Sandys statement was made in 1957 that there would be no further manned fighter aircraft (*see page 107*). This effectively put a stop on further developments for a crucial few years, other than those funded by the company itself.

The 'Hunter' was always commended for its graceful lines which made it one of the most shapely and handsome of aircraft. There is an interesting story around one particular aspect of the design recounted by an old retired draughtsman, the 'Hunter' wing tip shape. Camm appeared in the Drawing Office in his usual way one day as one of the draughtsmen was drawing up the wing tip plan shape. However, by now it had been decided that the aileron was too small and the area should be increased. This would result in the outer hinge point being moved outboard and a new wing tip shape was needed to fair this in. Several times the draughtsman lightly sketched in possible shapes using the different French curves available, rubbing out after inspecting the result, until Camm was happy with the final result. And so the 'Hunter' wing tip planform was decided. Fortunately it was aerodynamically satisfactory when the prototype finally flew, and certainly was a pleasing shape. However, this means of derivation could have been fraught with problems by such a random approach had the shape caused some aerodynamic problems, but this was before the days of computer analysis of airflow patterns over wings.

Nowadays aircraft design is more sensitive to such matters. A random choice based on personal preference for good looks is not the criterion in use, but Camm being of the old school, stuck rigidly to his personal choice for such decisions. If it looked good to him, it was good enough to give him the performance he expected of the aircraft.

Little episodes such as this were noticed by some of the design staff, particularly those who came into personal contact with him. They began to wonder if he was on top of matters technical. However, whether by luck or otherwise, invariably the decisions taken at his behest were acceptable for implementation but as the technological complexity of fast aeroplanes increased some of his fellow Directors began to wonder if there might be problems ahead.

The lack of a supersonic successor was not an oversight by Camm for, with the 'Hunter' being prepared for full production, he had turned his mind to such a design based on the 'Hunter'. The Americans had had the 'F-86 Sabre' in service since 1949 and were developing a successor, the 'F-100 Super Sabre', which was supersonic in level flight. The 'Hunter', like the 'F-86', was transonic, but only in a shallow dive at altitude.

Camm therefore, in late 1950, had ordered the Project Office to start scheming a development of the 'Hunter' with a 50 degree swept thin wing and a reheated

Hawker 'Hunters' demonstrate a formation loop. This emphasizes the excellent handling
qualities of the design.   *BAE Systems*

Avon engine of considerably increased power. This was designated the 'P.1083'. The Ministry showed interest and by 1951 the design was sufficiently advanced to enable the construction of a prototype. Meantime, the tooling up for 'Hunter' production was under way at Kingston and Coventry. The first production version, Kingston-built, flew from Dunsfold on 16th May, 1953.

The 'P.1083' was planned to be flying before the SBAC display at Farnborough, but in June of that year the Air Staff withdrew its support of the project. The three-quarters completed prototype was scrapped but some elements of the programme were preserved and fed into the 'Hunter' developments to come. It has been said that had the P.1083 come along, sales of the non-supersonic 'Hunter' may well have been compromised. 'Hunter' production was all tooled up and any change would have been very costly and delayed delivery.

Shortly after the prototype 'Hunter' made its first flight, another event gave Camm considerable pleasure when a grand-daughter, Elizabeth, was born to Phyllis and her husband, who had by now dropped his musician's role and was a solicitor's clerk. This addition to the family, to be their only grandchild, delighted Sydney and Hilda and was to give them much pleasure particularly as Phyllis and her husband were then living at 'Carradale' in Thames Ditton.

A significant event took place in September when the 'Hunter' prototype, suitably modified with a sharper nose profile, increased sweep on the canopy front and a reheated Avon engine, achieved the world absolute speed record of 727.6 mph, as well as the record for the 100 kilometre closed circuit course of 709.2 mph. Neville Duke was the pilot for both events.

However, the achievement of this record was not without its problems, as the aircraft to be used was on the charge of the Ministry, who had to be persuaded to relinquish control of it to enable the necessary modifications and trials to be carried out. This was eventually arranged and, once the modifications were made it was based at Dunsfold prior to being flown to Tangmere from where the record flights were to take place over the course along the South Coast between Bognor and Shoreham.

So, on 7th September, 1953, Duke flew the specially-modified aircraft to the RAF station at Tangmere in West Sussex which was conveniently close to the South Coast. The 'Hunter' had a fairly restricted fuel capacity and, with reheat in operation, the least fuel was required to fly to and from the course over which the runs were to be made. The official record then stood with the USA in the form of the North American 'F-86 Sabre' fighter which had achieved 670 mph, although a more recent unofficial attempt by Colonel Barnes of the United States Air Force had produced an average speed of 715 mph, also in a 'Sabre'. This latter, not being carried out under the auspices of the Fédération Aéronautique Internationale (FAI), was not recognised, but set a minimum value to be achieved and, if possible, bettered. It was.

However, there is an account of the first record attempt that needs to be inserted here, it not generally being known that a problem occurred after take-off. Duke was accelerating and climbing away after take-off, when there was a loud bang followed by severe vibration from the port wing. He could not see any reason from the cockpit, but the red warning light for the left main undercarriage

The two-seat 'Hunter' prototype. The side-by-side seating is apparent, a feature which did not affect the performance very much despite the extra frontal area, which helped the drag by imparting a measure of area-ruling to the aircraft.

BAE Systems

was lit, indicating that it was not locked up. The aircraft was still flyable so he elected to divert to Dunsfold and prepared to land there. On selecting undercarriage down only the nose and starboard main gear locked down, the left gear came down but swung in the airflow unlocked. Seeing it was impossible to lock the left main wheel, Duke elected to carry out the landing as best he could on the nose and right wheels. He approached the runway in a shallow powered glide to touch down gently on the two locked wheels. He held the left wing off the runway until the aileron effectiveness died away as speed reduced until it dropped which caused it to ground-loop and come to a halt on the grass beside the runway. Damage was confined to the left wing-tip.

Investigation of the damaged aircraft revealed the cause to be a fault in the undercarriage sequencing which resulted in the left main door shutting before the undercarriage came up, onto the outside of the door. Once this had been located the problem was resolved by a modification, Mod40, applied to all future production aircraft. Within a few days the damaged wing was rebuilt and the aircraft returned to Tangmere for the record attempt, which produced the necessary flights to obtain the speed record.

1953, in the middle of the 'Hunter' story, was a special year for both Camm and Sopwith, for in the Coronation Honours List of that year they were both given knighthoods. Their respective skills, Camm's of aircraft design leadership and Sopwith's of industrial management had contributed to the extensive growth of the Hawker Aircraft Company into the vast Hawker Siddeley empire, which then controlled much of the aviation expertise of the United Kingdom, was at last recognized.

Also, as matters proceeded to get the 'Hunter' ready for production, Sir Sydney was persuaded to accept the Presidency of the Royal Aeronautical Society for the 1954-1955 year. In many ways he rather enjoyed his time in that office, particularly on those occasions when Lady Camm could be at his side. His presidential year was highlighted by the 10th British Commonwealth Lecture which was given that year by HRH Prince Philip. Sir Sydney always disliked public appearances, but his sense of duty to the RAeS took precedence and all went well as he presented HRH with the scroll of Honorary Fellowship of the society at that event.

In this year he was further honoured by the award of the FAI Paul Tissandier Diploma as: 'One of the great aeronautical engineers of his country; the originator of aircraft such as the Hawker "Hurricane" and "Hunter"'.

1955 also saw Camm make his one and only visit to the North American continent. This was in company with other Hawker Siddeley Directors on a visit to Avro Aircraft in Canada, with calls at New York and Washington en route. They travelled over the Atlantic in style, on the *Queen Mary* and, apart from one short internal flight, the overland segments were covered by rail. In those days one of the stipulations of entry to the USA was that one must have been inoculated against smallpox. Camm had not been inoculated and steadfastly refused to allow this as his unorthodox views on physical illness meant that he did not consider this necessary. One way out of this impasse was to have an 'Ambassador's explanation' in his passport. Representation at the London Embassy of the USA achieved this requirement and the visit duly took place.

The later Mk V 'Hunters' became very effective fighter-bombers. A typical load of 24 3-inch rockets and two long range tanks is shown here.   *BAE Systems*

'Hunter' F Mk VI with long range tanks and outer wing weapons stations.   *BAE Systems*

In April 1954, Sir Sydney had ordered the Project Office to commence work on the latest operational requirement for a new fighter. The 'P.1103', as it became known, was chosen for submission from three designs studied in detail and in January the next year a specification, F135T, based on the earlier operational requirement, was received. Work continued until by October Hawker's tender was submitted to the Ministry. Despite learning that the tender was not successful in April 1956, the company took the decision to go ahead with refining the design and the construction of a prototype. The project was then renumbered as P.1121 and the Board decided to continue the building of the prototype at the company's own expense. The definitive aircraft was to be powered by a de Havilland 'Gyron' engine which, it was estimated, should give it a speed of Mach 2.5 at altitude. However, there were some disturbing moves on the political scene to come in 1957, which were to alter the picture completely.

It cannot be stated too strongly how detrimental the Sandys 1957 White Paper statement on the future of military aviation was to the UK aviation industry. This was that future manned aircraft would no longer be needed as the new guided weapons took over our air defence needs. The English Electric 'P.1', to become the 'Lightning', would be the last manned interceptor to be employed by the RAF. This was fanciful thinking and totally failed to realise that missiles, with huge development costs and expensive back-up equipment, were going to be as expensive, and probably more expensive, to develop than the aircraft they were intended to replace. Additionally there was no sign that any other country was going to adopt such a stance. In fact, Sir Sydney was not surprised by the policy stated, for in March he had met with the Deputy Chief of the Air Staff and found matters on the requirements for future manned aircraft very gloomy indeed. This was in line with the anticipated cuts in defence expenditure known to be on the Government's agenda.

The effect on the UK aircraft industry was catastrophic. Matters associated with the continued development of future generations of conventional manned aircraft slowed down as the companies affected planned ahead or were hit by cancellations of well-advanced programmes. The Project Offices still turned their minds to manned aircraft and kept the thinking for future developments alive. However, there was a distinct lack of Ministry encouragement and finance for prototypical exercises. The civil side of the Industry had been dealt a severe blow earlier by the 'Comet' disasters and a very promising programme of future development there took time to recover and advance again.

But to return to the Kingston scene in the Project Office. With the demise of the 'P.1121' after it had shown itself not capable of meeting a drastically revised operational requirement, the design by 1958 was dead as a project. The prototype was about 60 per cent complete and was scrapped. The Project Office then started scheming an enlarged twin engined derivative, the 'P.1125', for the revised operational requirement, which eventually turned into the 'P.1129', which was put forward as a possible contender for the requirement. Sir Sydney was told in confidence in July 1958 that it had already been decided to award any contract to a consortium of Vickers and English Electric. This gave rise to his oft-repeated remark that: 'Aircraft of the future will have to possess a fourth dimension - politics'. The resulting design eventually to come from this consortium was the ill-fated 'TSR2', which itself suffered cancellation at the whim of politicians. However, this disappointment was put to one side when Camm was informed by the RAeS of their award to him of the Society Gold Medal for that year.

The 'Hunter' was still in production, with some sizeable export orders materializing, as these events occurred and it was this that kept Hawker's afloat at a time when any loss of production could have been catastrophic for the company. Despite the fact that the 1957 Government pronouncement caused the cancellation of the last 100 'Hunters' for the RAF, such was the popularity of this outstanding combat and ground attack aircraft that two foreign customers, Sweden and India, stepped in and placed substantial orders ensuring that the production line continued without a break. The only real casualty was the Hawker Siddeley plant at Blackpool, which had been expressly bought to provide extra production space for the 'Hunter'.

However, the cancellation of the last batch of 'Hunters' for the RAF did eventually result in later years in the RAF having to deal with a shortage of 'Hunters' by organizing the purchase back of aircraft from abroad to be refurbished and delivered to the squadrons needing them.

In all, nearly 2,000 'Hunters' were built and sold, making it the most prolific of all British post-war military aircraft. Like several of its forebears, the 'Hunter', although starting as an interceptor, had also been developed as a ground attack machine, as which it was most successful. In fact, at the time of writing, the Lebanese Air Force has just resurrected six 'Hunters' from storage since 1996, to serve again in the rather volatile Middle Eastern situation.

This view of a 'Hunter' shows the under-fuselage air brake, a retrospective modification for all aircraft.   *BAE Systems*

Chapter Nine

The Final Fling

One particular feature of Sir Sydney's design leadership was that, as soon as new type of aircraft was in production, he would be considering schemes for a successor using such improvements, either in the power-plant, structurally or aerodynamically, as were being proposed. This forward-looking trait was one reason why Hawker's were able to produce something better as each new design appeared. Whilst not innovating new ideas himself, Sir Sydney was always ready to adopt them once proven elsewhere. He relied much upon advice from the research establishments like the NPL or RAE when he was deciding on their implementation in his designs. The 'P.1127' was a design which broke away from this philosophy as it was so revolutionary it could not follow the normal trend - there was no organization around which had any research programme remotely similar. The challenge was there.

In 1954, Dr A.A. Griffith, the Chief Scientist at Rolls-Royce, Derby, was advocating a Mach 2 supersonic airliner capable of vertical take-off and landing. His scheme had batteries of dedicated lift engines buried in the delta wings outboard of the passenger cabin and two banks of propulsion engines mounted in fin like structures at the rear. The author well remembers being given the task of analyzing this proposal at Hatfield in 1958. The concept was feasible but the sheer complexity of the 60 lift engines installed made matters somewhat daunting to contemplate from a maintenance standpoint.

The Rolls-Royce 'Flying Bedstead' was also at work making the news headlines and being demonstrated at the SBAC show. Vertical take-off and landing (VTOL) was around the corner and Project Offices throughout the UK were busy investigating the possibilities for the future. The Ministry of Supply even got involved and issued a specification ER143T for a jet-lift research aircraft. Rolls-Royce were actively developing a lift engine, the 'RB108', and the Kingston Project Office, in odd moments, was also active in looking at the possibility of VTOL, as was its equivalent at the de Havilland project group at Hatfield. The early studies involved multiple lift engines and separate propulsion engines which, although feasible, were hardly suitable for the fast agile fighter roles. Sir Sydney could see no purpose in carrying around the dead weight of lift engines in a combat situation. What was needed was a new approach to the power-plant situation.

With the successes of the 'Hart', 'Hurricane' and 'Hunter' to his name, Sir Sydney had proved to all his contemporaries that his grasp of the intricacies of aircraft design and development was one of the most reliable throughout the aircraft industry. As one type succeeded the other, he was firmly at the helm. His approach to each design was a cautious one, always treading the path of straightforward and recognized design methods. Innovation was rarely countenanced, he had to be given a very convincing argument to get his approval for anything new or out-of-the-ordinary. Hawker aircraft, up to this point in time, were sound practical designs, easy to manufacture and rugged machines. Despite there being competitive types for many of the requirements, the quality and dependability of Hawker types saw off some very potent alternatives. Sir Sydney's reputation often had a deciding vote when it came to the final selection. He was an acknowledged specialist in the design of fighters and ground-attack aircraft, who took great pains to ensure that his team produced the best possible answer to the specifications given them.

As for unorthodox schemes, these were not Sir Sydney's trait, so when it came to the idea of using vectored thrust to achieve short take-offs and landings, he viewed this with some misgivings. Although he could see the merits of such a scheme, it produced a design alien to his previous graceful conventional aircraft, and it took some persuasion to arouse his interest. This occurred in the following manner, and the net result was a unique aircraft, the 'Harrier'.

In the spring of 1957 the Bristol Aero-Engine Company produced a study, based on a turbo-fan version of their 'Orpheus' jet engine, of a power-plant capable of giving a vertical thrust component via rotating nozzles which could deflect the fan airflow downwards. The paper engine was given the designation BE53 and a brochure was issued.

The annual Paris Le Bourget air show took place that year as usual in early June and Sir Sydney flew over to cast his eyes over the latest developments on show. He was conducted around by Gerry Morel, a partner in the agency looking after the Hawker Aircraft affairs in France. As they walked around the French answer to the 'Flying Bedstead', the 'Flying Atar' was airborne nearby. This was basically a vertically-mounted jet engine assembly which could be hovered and 'flown' around to a limited extent as could its British counterpart. Morel asked Sir Sydney if he had seen the Bristol BS53 brochure. Receiving a negative reply, Morel saw to it that a copy was forwarded to Kingston without delay. This was passed to the Project Office where a member of his team, Ralph Hooper, soon produced a rough scheme for an observation and battlefield liaison aircraft. This appeared at the end of June, so clearly Sir Sydney was wanting an answer quickly, despite the fact that one man was on the job part time.

At this stage of the proceedings the exhaust from the turbine, or hot end, of this engine was not deflected, which put constraints on the design possibilities and direct vertical take-off and landing was not possible.

However, by now, Sir Sydney was more interested in this new engine, and sensed that there might be some potential in it, as could his project team. He wrote to Dr Hooker of Bristol Engines who visited Kingston on 25th June, so matters clearly were moving forward.

The thinking up to now was still concentrated on the battlefield liaison aircraft but the inability to use all the thrust components vertically hampered progress. Ralph Hooper then had a flash of inspiration, he suggested that if the turbine exhaust could be split, as on the 'Sea Hawk', it should be possible to deflect this downwards either side of the fuselage using similar nozzles as for the front fan exhaust. He put this to Sir Sydney who arranged a visit to Bristol Engines to get their reaction.

At the end of July Hooper was at Bristol's expounding the idea. Gordon Lewis of that firm agreed to add testing of this arrangement to tests already planned for the cold nozzles. And so was born the idea of the 'Pegasus' engine with its unique four nozzle configuration.

The battlefield liaison aircraft project was altered to one of ground attack/reconnaissance purposes and given the project number 'P.1127'. This, after extensive development, was to become the 'Harrier'. August was a busy month in the Project Office, for the SBAC show was due in early September and a brochure was needed covering the 1127.

The VTOL studies continued at a slow pace for some time, as other projects and on-going 'Hunter' work filled Sir Sydney's time. So it remained until 1959, and with his reputation bolstered by the success of the 'Hunter', Sir Sydney, now in his 66th year, showed no indication of the wish to retire. He was still a fit man and seemed determined to carry on ad infinitum. So his forays into the Drawing Office still continued and his ideas as to how the design should proceed were still paramount. The design and construction of the prototype 'P.1127' continued, with an anticipated completion by 1960.

In 1959 his brother Frederick, after a distinguished career as editor of several Newnes technical magazines, including all of the 'Practical' series, died on the 18th February from bronchial pneumonia. Frederick had been a good assistant to Sir Sydney back in those days when he was beginning his aeronautical adventures by building and flying the model aircraft. Several of these models still existed in Frederick's hands and Sir Sydney distributed them among the other Camm brothers as a memento to Frederick, whose life had not been very happy at times, particularly in 1939 when his wife had died followed by the death of his only son 'Little Fred' in 1957.

In 1960 Sir Sydney was made Chief Engineer of Hawker's, with Roy Chaplin his faithful and long-suffering assistant being promoted to Chief Designer as well as being elevated to the Board. Despite his promotion, Sir Sydney carried on as usual dictating the design matters, the other disciplines coming under the remit of a Chief Engineer not being his field. However, there were some disadvantages when a complex technical problem requiring computer analysis, or lengthy wind-tunnel or flight test investigations raised its head. Sir Sydney, whilst always managing to guide his team through the matrix of design methodology, appeared a bit out of his depth. Some were aware of his difficulty in the struggle to keep up with the considerable advances coming along and realized that the great man was finding himself technically behind the times. He was not the only one of his generation finding it difficult to cope. This did not daunt him one bit, he still was capable of providing a strong leadership and offering his advice where necessary.

It must have been difficult for Chaplin to stomach the continued presence of Sir Sydney on design matters. It was as though he could not hand on complete responsibility for such matters to someone who had been a faithful and competent assistant for so long. Chaplin lasted until 1962 before retiring early at the age of 63 due to ill health. He had spent 36 years with the company, the vast majority of it as Camm's number two.

However, with the vectored thrust concept accepted as a future design worthy of investigation Sir Sydney entered into the monitoring of the tasks associated with the project studies that emerged from this programme.

The tethered hover trials in the 'P.1127', Dunsfold October 1960.

As the 'Hunter' production line closed down the workshops were becoming under-used. And with no clear successor in sight, for the first time in its history the works at Richmond Road were reliant on outside top-up work to keep the skilled workforce occupied. This kept them together ready for the day when matters would return to normality.

Meantime, the Project Office was busy, with further studies of V/STOL aircraft, all of them having supersonic capabilities. The first was essentially a supersonic 'P.1127', the prototypes of the latter which were by now under construction as a private venture, with Sir Sydney insisting all along that simplicity be adopted.

Despite repeated approaches to the Ministry no support was forthcoming and construction of the prototypes continued. By now Bristol's had obtained funding from the USA to assist in the development of the engine to be used in the 'P.1127'. The engine had had its first bench run in September 1959, producing a thrust of 9,000 lb. A further engine was prepared for Hawker's first prototype and delivered in early 1960.

Whilst all the development of the 'P.1127' was proceeding, the Project Office was more busy. Sir Sydney was now convinced that the V/STOL concept was feasible and his project team continued investigating the possibility of a supersonic design. In 1961 the 'P.1150' study emerged. Several variants of this were studied with more powerful engines, one with extra lift engines to boost the lifting capability in the hover, but no interest could be generated. The political scene was such that expensive new developments were not popular, so Sir Sydney's earlier pronouncement about the 'extra dimension' was now a key feature. The simple straightforward 'P.1127' project continued and, on 21st October, 1960, the first hover flight had been achieved at Dunsfold. For this achievement the aircraft had been stripped of all non-essential equipment to lighten it as much as possible and was kept from lifting more than a few feet by restraining cables anchored to a specially prepared grid on the airfield. Occasional sudden calls for control inputs were part and parcel of the 'flight' leading Bill Bedford, the chief test pilot, to remark that these tethered hovers were similar to learning to ride a bicycle down a narrow corridor in the dark. Then somebody suddenly realized that the cause for the problem was the restraining tugs on the tethering cables as the aircraft reached the limits of their length. Just prior to these first hovers the Ministry of Supply had issued contract cover for the prototypes, so Hawker's at last had the backing of the appropriate authorities for their unique design.

Further hover tests were carried out and by 19th November the restraints were removed and a completely free hover achieved satisfactorily. The project was now proving its viability. Following this some taxiing tests were carried out and some conventional flights made from the long runway at RAE Bedford during which the aircraft was put through a test programme taking it through speeds up to 400 knots, 4 'g' loading and up to 30,000 ft altitude. Then the first prototype was joined by the second aircraft. It was not until 7th July, 1961 that the second prototype got airborne and the two aircraft now available to go through a test programme aimed at closing the gap between engine-borne hover and wing-borne normal flight, which was achieved by 8th September. By 12th September the development pilots, Bill Bedford and Hugh Merewether, were making complete accelerating and decelerating transitions between both modes of flight. V/STOL had arrived and official backing was now appearing, with the Americans showing great interest in continuing to support this revolutionary concept. All this initial flying had been done with the early Bristol engine and by now, encouraged by the positive results being achieved, Bristol's were making plans to produce a more powerful version, talking in terms of 18,000 lb. thrust.

Sir Sydney had, throughout the development and flight trials of the prototypes, been making representations to his contacts in Ministry circles. He, himself, was now convinced of the viability of V/STOL and could see a future for the concept. His standing in the Ministry was such that the company finally prised the money from the Treasury to back the development of the 'P.1127'. There were things he did not like about the design but accepted them as inevitable, after all it was a radical departure from the accepted standards of his earlier years.

As the 'P.1127' proved itself and the interest grew in the concept, Sir Sydney saw to it that the Project Office kept up a steady flow of studies. By 1961 the Navy indicated an interest in the V/STOL concept and the 'P.1152' Naval V/STOL strike fighter was proposed by Hawker's. This was much more complex than the simple 'P.1127' in that it employed four lift engines to augment the lift/cruise engine yet was still shown on the official drawings with an arrester hook!

The 'P.1127' concept fired the imaginations of many other organizations, amongst which was NATO. The flexibility offered by the ability to operate out of confined spaces led to the production of a Requirement for a supersonic vertical/short take-off aircraft, the NATO Basic Military Requirement No. 3 (NBMR3). To meet this Requirement further project work was expended with the 1150 which went through two variants, ending up as the 'P.1150/3', later renumbered 'P.1154'.

This resulted in the 'P.1154' design being put forward as Hawker's submission, competing with some 10 other designs entered by other European and US companies. With the by now established fact of a successful 'P.1127' the 'P.1154' was the technical winner of that competition. Politics entered the fray again and the French Dassault 'Mirage IIIV' looked as though it would be the final selected winner. However, the programme folded up after a fatal accident in 1966 of one of the two prototypes. It had shortly before that become the first VTOL fighter to achieve Mach 2, although if the 'P.1154' had been built it should also have been capable of a speed not much less than that. However, the '1154' died later due to the rather crazy idea of merging its NATO requirements with a current RN requirement for a carrier-borne similar type.

With Hawker's continual pressure for the Ministry to observe the potential of the 'P.1127', by 1962 note had been taken of this in the United States and Germany. Coupled with this was the 'P.1154' design which was being tendered to the Ministry as a firm proposal. The result was an order from the Ministry for nine development examples of the 'P.1127' to equip a tri-partite squadron to be formed with pilots from the RAF, US Navy, USAF, US Army and the Luftwaffe. This organization was funded by the three countries and its task was to determine the feasibility of operating V/STOL aircraft for a range of roles, concentrating on take-off and landing techniques, jet-borne handling, instrument flying and night flying techniques.

The aircraft provided for this exercise were considerably different from the prototype 'P.1127', with a new wing and tailplane, revised front fuselage and intake, and was named the 'Kestrel'. It also incorporated a much improved and up-rated 'Pegasus Mk V' engine.

From the knowledge gleaned on this collaborative exercise, the Americans were very keen to consider adopting V/STOL and, after the end of the test programme carried out by the tripartite squadron, took six of the 'Kestrels' to the USA, where it was ultimately given the designation XV-6A. Germany, however, dropped out and went their own way, never adopting V/STOL in service aircraft.

The remaining two 'Kestrels' (one had been involved in an accident during the Tripartite trials and was never replaced) stayed in the UK to be used by the Ministry on V/STOL flight operations.

But in 1964 the general election returned a socialist government which proceeded to wreak havoc in the UK aircraft industry by cancelling some vital defence projects. Out went the 'P.1154', the 'TSR2' and 'AW681' short take-off and landing (STOL) freighter. In came the 'F-111' fiasco and the re-engined (Rolls-Royce Spey) Phantom to fill some of the void. The 'F-111' was ordered then cancelled resulting in multi-million payments to cover cancellation costs, but the Phantom order went ahead. Somehow the 'P.1127' weathered the storm and a pre-production order for the derivative was to appear. There were, however, some inevitable lay-offs at Kingston but the design team so carefully built up was kept largely together.

At the end of 1965 the 'P.1127' was given a massive boost when a contract arrived from the Ministry for a development batch of six aircraft, which was to be followed by an initial order for 60 aircraft. The name eventually selected was the 'Harrier', but not until after the first flight of the first development batch example. Prior to that the designation had been 'P.1127' (RAF).

Despite his lack of academic qualifications, Sir Sydney had enough experience to make sound judgments on the design aspects of the increasingly complex aircraft that came from his teams. Where he really scored was the fact

The fourth of the six 'P.1127' prototypes, XP976.   *BAE Systems*

The fifth prototype 'P.1127', XP980.

that he had become a figurehead in the aerospace industry, and was respected for that, having made his name with some outstanding designs. He had acquired a great number of colleagues in various Ministries and specialist organizations such as the RAE and NPL who respected his keen judgment and were often available to support his cause.

In 1963 Sir Sydney became Director of Design for Hawker Siddeley Aviation and was made a Director of the Hawker Siddeley Group. This made no difference to his appearances in the Design Department. Despite reaching the age of 70 that year he continued at his Richmond Road office as usual each day, seemingly uninterested in retirement.

In late 1965 Sir Sydney learnt that he had been awarded the Daniel Guggenheim Medal for that year. This was a great honour indeed and his name was added to a distinguished list of recipients such as Orville Wright, Geoffrey de Havilland, Frank Whittle, F.W. Lanchester, Donald Douglas, and William Boeing, to name but a few. The medal itself had been established by Daniel Guggenheim and his son Harry and was first awarded in 1929 and has been given yearly since then. The full citation for Sir Sydney's award reads: 'For over 50 years continuous dedication to the design of Military aircraft and pioneering of many new concepts and the creation of many successful aircraft, representative of the best tradition of British design skill'. However, events were to prevent him receiving this great honour in person.

On the afternoon of Friday 11th March, 1966, Sir Sydney made one of his regular visits to the Drawing Office to look over the drawings for the modification to the 'P.1127' tailplane, which had been increased in span to help with control problems found with the original design. This modification, entailing an extension to the span resulting in a slight kink in the leading edge, worried him as he thought it inelegant and the members of his team gathered round the drawing board to argue the case for no further change to the modified component. Sir Sydney argued forcefully for a neater answer but was repeatedly told that any major change as suggested by him would require a brand-new item which would be too expensive, bearing in mind that the current contract with the Ministry was fixed price. He eventually gave up trying to have his way and retired, saying: 'We'll come back to this again. I don't feel up to it today'. With that he returned to his office and, after clearing up the current business, went home for the weekend.

The next day he was out on Richmond Park golf course playing a round when, suddenly, he collapsed and died. The inquest showed the cause of death as Hypertension (high blood pressure). A master of design had gone. He was 72, an age when most would have been retired for some years.

The funeral took place the following week, with many colleagues and friends present, followed by the interment in the churchyard at Long Ditton where, in recent times, the tombstone of Sir Sydney and Lady Camm has been restored by the Hawker Association.

The Guggenheim award ceremony was held at an aviation conference in New York on the 28th April, a few weeks after Sir Sydney's sudden death, and the British Ambassador to the United States received it on behalf of Lady Camm from Grover Loening, himself a famous pioneer of aviation.

The original Hawker factory in Canbury Park Road, Kingston. An aerial view taken in the 1990s before the main factory building was demolished. The flat-roofed brick building in the lower centre contained the experimental department where the 'Hurricane' prototype took shape.
BAE Systems

There was a memorial service for Sir Sydney in the summer of 1966, held appropriately at St Clement Dane's Church with its string of connections to the Royal Air Force. An address was given by Sir Thomas Sopwith in which he said:

> Undoubtedly he was the greatest designer of fighter aircraft the world has ever known. He had a wonderful character - forceful to a degree when he was right but always ready to listen to another point of view on the rare occasions he was wrong. Outside his profession he was modest and self-effacing, enjoying the simplest of pleasures and never asking more of life than the warmth of his family, his friends and the occasional round of golf.

The church was full, with Sir Sydney's colleagues from work, from the aircraft industry and acquaintances from the many Government departments with which he had dealt over many years, in addition to members of his family, who all mourned the passing of a truly great man.

On 21st July, 2006, forty years after the St Clement Dane's service, a further memorial service was held at the parish church of St John the Baptist in Windsor to commemorate the life of a famous engineer in the town where he was born. At this event a plaque in his memory was unveiled by his great-grand-daughter, Miss Chloe Barratt-Dickson and a fitting tribute to his life and work came from Air Chief Marshal Sir Joe French. Sir Sydney's grand-daughter Elizabeth also spoke, reminiscing about her grandfather in her younger days when he would drive over and read her a bedtime story and, later, take her to Paris for a celebration holiday after she passed her 11-plus exam.

Kingston continued on without the great man, who had been such a figure-head and leader for over 40 years. Just six months after his death, the first development batch 'Harrier' made its first flight and in April 1968 the first production batch entered service as the 'GR Mk 1' with No. 1 Squadron of RAF Strike Command. The 'P.1127', or 'Harrier' as it is more commonly known, continued development and proved its worth in both air combat and ground attack roles in the Falklands War and as a ground attack aircraft in both Gulf Wars. Today the 'Harrier GR7', as the latest variant of a family of short take off and vertical landing (STOVL) service aircraft, it serves as an effective ground attack type in Afghanistan. Sir Sydney would have been proud of the creditable performance of this last creation to come to fruition under him, as he would have been over the 'Hawk' advanced jet trainer now serving in over a dozen Air Forces around the world. This latter design has now reached a total of 32 years in production and looks set to continue thus for many more years. Many aspects of the Camm tradition have lived on, passed down through the team at Kingston until its removal to Farnborough after the closure in 1991 of that historic site. For three-quarters of a century, Kingston produced some of the most effective fighter aircraft to provide the RAF with the means of combatting offensive air forces. In all, a total of some 45,000 aircraft, of which 27,000 were products designed or influenced by Sir Sydney Camm, had resulted from the Kingston team's efforts over those years. What better legacy could an outstanding aircraft designer want?

Sir Sydney Camm, *c.*1953.   *BAE Systems*

Chapter Ten

Camm, The Man

The foregoing narrative has only touched lightly on Camm as a person, and then only in the context of him at work. There are other aspects of his life, some of them outside the work environment, which need recording and, rather than scatter them through the story, they are put down here to give a fuller picture of a man dedicated to his work when in the office, yet able to switch off outside and become absorbed with the everyday matters of home and leisure pursuits.

Despite his elevation to the highest office the Royal Aeronautical Society could offer, that of the President, a Directorship of a leading aircraft manufacturer and a Knighthood, Camm could not be persuaded to give lectures to Learned Societies, rarely produced any articles for professional publications and, most certainly, never allowed himself to be interviewed. In this context, his modesty was part of his overall character, a fact which many found unusual for such an outspoken person.

As an old Project Office man recounted to the author, when Sir Sydney was on the prowl, one kept one's head down and waited for the comment from him. He would position himself behind the person of interest and peer over at the work under way. A query would often as not be prefixed by a 'Harrumph' before the interrogation started. If explanation as to what was going on was needed the request came directly to that person, rather than through the appropriate section leader. The dress code in the offices was also watched and on one occasion at least, when a member of staff appeared without a tie, he was ordered to go home and put one on immediately, being told: 'Our customers often come here to see us, and that includes our appearance'.

For those who worked under Sydney Camm, life in the Design Office could sometimes be difficult, especially if they questioned his orders. Like many a genius, Camm was underneath, a basically shy person whose enthusiasm sometimes boiled over into rather outspoken comments when emphasizing his will. One day he could be almost diffident about the current design matters, but this could change to an autocratic, or so it seemed, stance when a problem raised its head.

Despite the difficulties experienced by his staff due to his sometimes overbearing nature, when things were going well he could be the picture of affability, and he gained their respect, particularly if countering outside criticism aimed at them. His defence of them was forthright but rarely, if ever, admitted to them. He clearly recognized the fact that ultimately his position was dependent upon their actions and his support of them was crucial to maintain their absolute loyalty.

On top of his support when needed, the staff, once they had got to know his foibles and dislikes, knew that here was a man of absolute integrity, an honest man with a directness of purpose in life. Perhaps the following story will illustrate the concern he had for those of his staff for whom he had considerable respect. One of his senior draughtsmen had, in passing, mentioned a desire to go and work in North America. Camm called him in and talked matters over in general terms, during which he learnt that despite several letters to various aircraft companies in Canada and the United States from this person, no offers of employment had resulted. He accordingly wrote off to Avro Canada to ask if that company had any vacancies for experienced draughtsmen. Shortly after this the draughtsman received an offer of employment from Avro Canada. Camm's recommendation and enquiry had done the trick. He accepted the offer and went over to get established before bringing his family over. Upon arrival he assessed the situation at Avro Canada and quickly realised he had made a mistake. He duly returned to the UK and started looking for work and was on the point of accepting an offer, when the phone rang. It was Camm to say that he had heard that he was back in the country and to ask if he would like to come back to Kingston. If yes, an offer letter would be in the post that evening. This episode is typical of Camm and his concern for the ambitions of those bright young men in his team.

Sir Sydney's father had prided himself on his handwork, accuracy and quality in his tasks as carpenter and joiner. He impressed these attributes of his skills on his sons from early on in their lives. So far as Sir Sydney was concerned, he was to take all this to heart in his chosen career and insist on accuracy and quality in the work of his staff.

With his carefully selected senior staff Camm could often be the epitome of kindness and courtesy, and seemed able to show great pleasure at his own enthusiastic outspoken comments made during design meetings or social occasions. Yet, despite all this, there was an underlying modesty which brought a human touch to his dealings. A complex man when deeply engaged in his tasks.

It must be said of those who worked under Camm, the experience and advice they picked up served them well in later life when they had moved away to other jobs. By the 1950s the large number of ex-Hawker design employees to be found in charge of other design organizations is a testament to his guidance and advice when they had been in the Design and Project Offices at Kingston.

One other reason which contributed to the Hawker team's success was Camm's insistence on keeping it small. This enabled the individual members to keep personal contacts easily thereby making the interchange of ideas more effective. For instance, as the 'Hunter' was being developed as a prototype the design staff available numbered a little over 200 and, during the war years, had peaked at about 320. Of course, this was well before the entry of some vital specialist tasks such as the complex avionics and weapon systems which now constitute such an important part of any military aircraft.

He always showed little interest in the rather shabby offices he occupied at Canbury Park Road. So long as he could sit there in the relative comfort of familiar surroundings and formulate his thoughts or venture out to the design office next door to do his daily round of the boards and discuss crucial matters with members of his team, he was content.

When away from his office he would often be up at the Air Ministry sounding out his contacts there to get a feel for the current thinking on specific contracts or particular specifications being worked on. In the context of the choice of power-plants he could often be found with Major Bulman, the Director of aero-engine development and production, mulling over the choice of new engines on offer, more particularly during the years from 1935 to 1945. Camm and Bulman clearly got on well with each other, not only respecting each other's expertise, but also having common ground in that they both had been visitors to Brooklands in the years before World War I to witness many of the early aviators exhibiting their skills. They had first met up during the Lympne Light Aircraft trials in 1924.

Whilst in the context of his Ministry contacts, it is relevant to include a quote from Sir Thomas Sopwith in relation to this, again from the St Clement Dane address:

> Many people think that a design starts with a specification from the authorities, but with Camm this procedure was reversed. He considered that the uninterrupted experience he had in fighter design over a number of years enabled him to forecast the RAF's next requirement better than they could themselves. In other words he would produce a new design, incorporating various features which he knew the Air Ministry wanted, discuss it at length with the Air Ministry (and later the Ministry of Supply) and in due course an official specification would be issued largely written around the tentative specification he had originally submitted. This happened time and time again ...

At home, Camm was devoted to his wife Hilda, daughter Phyllis and to his only grandchild, Elizabeth, and was very much an ordinary settled and happy person. His family life was to him, a very important part of his life. So often we find matters distorted by references to his behaviour at work. It was not so at home where he felt relaxed away from the responsibilities and pressures at Hawker's. The Camms at home were not reclusive in any way, integrating with the local community socially. Sir Sydney was very popular with the ladies, who thought him: 'A lovely man, so polite and nice'.

He sometimes took problems from work home and, in odd moments, would sit in his study mulling over them. One day, during the early 'P.1127' design and development exercise, when he was settled thus, his grand-daughter Elizabeth wandered in and asked him what he was doing. 'I'm trying to design and aeroplane that doesn't need a runway'. she was told, followed by an explanation of the concept of vertical take-off in simple terms. He clearly was proud of this project, despite his often grumpy comments on '..b. Mother's pots and pans', referring to the rotating exhaust nozzles sticking out along the fuselage which were needed to give it the unique quality of hovering flight. It was this design which enabled the UK to provide the crucial air cover, in the form of the 'Sea Harrier', which ensured the success of the Falklands expedition.

The steadying influence of family life kept him focused on his occupation, which provided the means to keep them in the comforts of a good home. His interests in the evenings and at the weekends were wide. Reading, particularly novels by Damon Runyan and Evelyn Waugh, gave him great enjoyment as he relaxed at home. With a good sense of humour, he would recount some of the funnier episodes in the books for the family.

Music was another means of relaxing, but it had to be conventional orchestral pieces or similar and for some reason solo singers grated on his nerves. On some evenings at home he could be found meticulously painting some chairs or repairing shoes with stick-on soles and heels, this latter clearly a throw-back to his early days when money was short.

He also was a keen photographer, and those who have seen some of his pictures have said that they ranked as good as many to come from the professionals.

His one great sporting love was golf, and he had set to and taken that up with great determination. To his delight, he discovered himself to be a good player and would be found on the golf course at weekends playing a round. His handicap was eight, and he did like winning.

Hilda Camm would sometimes pick him up at the office in their car, and being a rather small lady it could look as though the waiting car was parked and empty. One day the Armstrong Siddeley was sitting outside in Canbury Park Road and Sydney appeared on his way home. Reaching the car he proceeded to go round it flicking off sundry bits of dust and fluff he found. Suddenly the car spoke: 'Sydney, what's wrong?' He stopped his inspection and got in to be driven home by Hilda.

Often, in his later years, he would drive to the golf course in his E-type Jaguar. Fast, high performance, cars were always one of his interests. Quite often, on a business trip, particularly down to Hawker's airfield at Dunsfold, he would stop in a country lane to pick a few wild flowers to take home to Hilda. These jaunts sometimes happened, more particularly in those years when the politicians were trying to influence the aircraft industry, if he was frustrated after a heavy session with his contacts at the Ministry. Somehow getting close to his creations and the men who flew them took his mind off the political scene which so often interfered with his flow of ideas.

In his later years, as his affluence increased, he showed a surprising lack of interest in his growing wealth. Money, to him, was useful enough but, as for investing it - he preferred the relative safety of the bank.

Also towards the final years he suddenly started taking ballroom dancing lessons, arriving at the Spencer-Bryant School of Dance in Surbiton for some private lessons with Hilda to practise the art, presumably to be used on social occasions. This was around the time of his Presidency of the Royal Aeronautical Society.

So far as his relationships with those responsible for other disciplines in the company, Camm's greatest accord was with the Flight Development Department in the shape of the test pilots who took his designs into the air to investigate the unknowns and provide corroboration of the performance estimates. He was always appreciative of their enthusiasm with which they undertook their sometimes dangerous work. He realized how much his team, and those of other designers, owed to their test pilots. This affinity to the many individuals who flew his planes was to continue all his life. Yet the times when he would get airborne, even for a passenger flight, were rare indeed long before the new monoplanes came along to supersede the biplanes of the 1920s and 1930s.

Although he had flown occasionally in his younger days, we have seen that in later years he could only in rare circumstances be persuaded to board an airliner for an overseas flight, and then only short haul. His one and only visit to North America during his working life was by sea on the *Queen Mary*. A bit of a paradox, but that was (Sir) Sydney Camm.

Appendix

'What hath God wrought?'

Extracts from the first published account of an eye-witness, Amos Ives Root, who was present on 20th September, 1904 to watch the first controlled powered flight over a circular path by the Wright Brothers 1904 'Flyer' at Huffman Prairie.

God in his great mercy has permitted me to be, at least somewhat, instrumental in ushering in and introducing to the great wide world an invention that may outrank electric cars, the automobiles, and all other methods of travel, and one which may fairly take a place beside the telephone and wireless telegraphy. It was my privilege, on the 20th day of September, 1904, to see the first successful trip of an airship, without a balloon to sustain it, that the world has ever made, that is, to turn the corners and come back to the starting point. When it first turned the circle, and came near the starting point, I was right in front of it; and I said then, and I believe still, it was one of the grandest sights, if not the grandest sight, of my life. Imagine a locomotive that has left its track and is climbing up in the air right towards you - a locomotive without any wheels, we will say, but with white wings instead. Well, now, imagine this white locomotive, with wings that spread 20 feet each way, coming right towards you with a tremendous flap of its propellers, and you will have something like what I saw. The younger brother bade me move to one side for fear it might come down suddenly; but I tell you friends, the sensation that one feels in such a crisis is something hard to describe. When Columbus discovered America he did not know what the outcome would be, and no one at the time knew. In a like manner these two brothers have probably not even a faint glimpse of what their discovery is going to bring to the children of men. No one living can give a guess of what is coming along this line. Possibly we may be able to fly over the North Pole, even if we should not succeed in tacking the Stars and Stripes to its uppermost end. But to me the sight of a machine like the one I have pictured, with its white canvas planes and rudders subject to human control, is one of the grandest and most inspiring sights I have ever seen on earth; and when you see one of these graceful crafts sailing over your head, and possibly over your home, as I expect you will in the near future, see if you don't agree with me that the flying machine is one of God's most gracious and precious gifts.

Amos Ives Root was successful and wealthy businessman - a Manufacturer of beekeeping equipment at a time when beekeeping was a more important part of American agriculture. In that field he was among the best known figures in the world. He was also a publisher, a writer, a temperance movement crusader and promoter of the Sunday School movement, a philanthropist, an inventor, a technology enthusiast and the leading citizen of his home town, Medina, Ohio.

Bibliography

Aeroplane Construction by Sydney Camm, Crosby Lockwood & Son, 1919.
Bulldog, the Bristol Bulldog Fighter by David Luff, Airlife Publishing Ltd., 1987.
Fellowship of the Air - Jubilee book of the Royal Aero Club by B.J. Hurren, Iliffe & Sons, 1951.
F.J. Camm - The Practical Man by Gordon G. Cullingham, published by the author, 1996.
Hawker Aircraft since 1920 by Francis K. Mason, Putnam Aeronautical Books, Third revised edition 1991.
Hawker - a Biography of Harry Hawker by L.K.Blackmore, Airlife Publishing Ltd, 1993.
Royal Air Force 1939-1945, The Fight at Odds, by Denis Richards, HMSO, 1954.
Spitfire, the Biography by Jonathan Glancy, Atlantic Books, 2006.
Sydney Camm and the Hurricane: Perspectives on the Master Fighter Designer and his Finest Achievement by J.W. Fozard (ed.), Airlife Publishing Ltd, 1991.
Test Pilot by Neville Duke, Allan Wingate, 1953.
The Magic of a Name - The Rolls-Royce Story - The First 40 Years by Peter Pugh, Icon Books, UK, 2000.
The Second World War - Volume 1, The Gathering Storm by Winston Churchill, Cassell & Co., 1948.
75 Years of Aviation in Kingston - 1913-1988, published by British Aerospace 1988.

Index